CW01095883

HEALTH POLICY, ETH
AND HUMAN VALUE
European and North American Perspectives

Conference Highlights, Papers and Conclusions

XXIst CIOMS Conference
Noordwijk aan Zee, The Netherlands
2–5 June 1987

Edited by Z. Bankowski and J.H. Bryant

CI MS

Geneva 1988

PROGRAMME COMMITTEE

Bankowski, Z. Executive Secretary, Council for International Organizations of Medical Sciences (CIOMS), Geneva

Bryant, J.H. Chairman; Professor, Aga Khan University, Karachi

Gorovitz, S. Dean, Syracuse University, Syracuse, New York

Krijnen, J.H. Staff Bureau for Health Policy Development, Ministry of Welfare, Health and Cultural Affairs, Rijswijk, Netherlands

de Wachter, M.A.M. Director, Netherlands Institute for Bioethics, Maastricht, Netherlands

van der Werff, A. Policy Advisor, Ministry of Welfare, Health and Cultural Affairs, Rijswijk, Netherlands

LOCAL ORGANIZING COMMITTEE, NETHERLANDS

Alkemade, A.M.C. International Health Affairs Division, Ministry of Welfare, Health and Cultural Affairs, Rijswijk

Krijnen, J.H. Chairperson; Staff Bureau for Health Policy Development, Ministry of Welfare, Health and Cultural Affairs, Rijswijk

Leenen, H.J.J. Institute of Social Medicine, University of Amsterdam; CIOMS Liaison Officer of the Royal Netherlands Academy of Sciences, Amsterdam

Noach, E.L Netherlands Institute for Bioethics, Maastricht; University of Leiden, Leiden

Veldkamp, H.R.G. Director, Health Care Professions and Training, Ministry of Welfare, Health and Cultural Affairs, Rijswijk

de Wachter, M.A.M. Co-Chairman; Director, Netherlands Institute for Bioethics, Maastricht

Wijnberg, B. Staff Bureau for Health Policy Development, Ministry of Welfare, Health and Cultural Affairs, Rijswijk

SPONSORS

This Conference was co-sponsored by the Ministry of Welfare, Health and Cultural Affairs of the Netherlands, the Institute for Bioethics, the Netherlands, and the World Health Organization.

TABLE OF CONTENTS

ACKNOWLEDGEMENTS vi
INTRODUCTION vii
INAUGURAL CEREMONY 1
    J. van Londen, Ministry of Welfare, Health and Culture,
    Rijswijk, Netherlands 1
    J.F. Dunne, World Health Organization, Geneva 4
    G. Pinet, WHO Regional Office for Europe, Copenhagen 6
    D. de Wied, Royal Netherlands Academy of Arts and Sciences,
    Amsterdam 8
    J.M. Bonnike, Noordwijk, Netherlands 9

HIGHLIGHTS OF THE NOORDWIJK CONFERENCE 11
    J.H. Bryant
    Background to the Conference 11
    Setting the Scene 16
    Themes of the Conference 20
    Reflections on the Conference 39
    Perspective on the Conference 46
    The Conference and WHO's Goal of Health for All 49
    Onward from Noordwijk — the Next Steps 51

PAPERS AND DISCUSSION 53
Interactions of Health Policy, Ethics and Human Values: A North
American Perspective
    S. Gorovitz 53

Interactions of Health Policy, Ethics and Human Values: A
European Perspective
    E. Kuuskoski-Vikatmaa 61

Screening and Counselling — Ethical and Policy Aspects
    M.A.M. de Wachter 67

Genetic Screening and Counselling — Implications of the DNA
Technologies
    M.F. Niermeijer 77

Screening and Counselling: Report of Discussion Group
    M.F. Niermeijer 91

Organ Transplantation — Ethical Issues
    F. Vilardell 95

Transplantation Policies
A. van der Werff 111

Organ Transplantation: Report of Discussion Group
A. van der Werff 127

Health Care of the Elderly — Ethical Issues
D. Callahan 131

Health Care of the Elderly — Quality of Life and Aging
Sir Douglas Black 137

Health Care of the Elderly: Report of Discussion Group
D. Callahan 143

Lifestyles and Health Hazards — Individual Choices and Collective Interests
M. Bégin 149

Community and Ethics in Lifestyle Changes
E.B. Fisher 159

Lifestyles and Health Hazards: Report of Discussion Group
E.B. Fisher 175

REFLECTIONS AND PERSPECTIVES 179
The Viewpoint of the Health Policymaker
E.W. Roscam Abbing 179

The Viewpoint of the Health Professional
S. Doxiadis 183

The Viewpoint of the Ethicist
S. Gorovitz 187

The Perspective of the Developing World
B.O. Osuntokun (Africa) 191
P. Ratanakul (Asia) 199

Perspective of an East-European Country — Poland
M. Sokolowska 203

Perspective of an East-European Country — The German
Democratic Republic
S.M. Rapoport 209

CLOSING OF THE CONFERENCE 213
    J. van Londen 213
    F. Vilardell 215

LIST OF CONFERENCE PARTICIPANTS 217

v

ACKNOWLEDGEMENTS

The Council for International Organizations of Medical Sciences (CIOMS) expresses its gratitude to the Ministry of Welfare, Health and Cultural Affairs of the Government of the Netherlands, and particularly to Dr J. Van Londen, Director-General for Health; Dr A. van der Werff, Policy Advisor; and Mrs J.H. Krijnen of the Staff Bureau for Health Policy Development, for their invaluable advice and contribution to the preparation of the Conference, and to Mrs A.M.C. Alkemade of the International Health Affairs Division, for her very efficient work in its technical preparation.

We acknowledge especially the contribution of Professor John H. Bryant in his leadership in the organization and chairmanship of the Conference and in the preparation of the highlights of the discussions, and that of Professor M.A.M. de Wachter for his help in the preparation of the programme. We owe a special debt to the authors of the papers; the chairmen and rapporteurs of the working groups and the chairmen of the plenary sessions; and Dr J. Gallagher for his assistance in the editing and preparation of this volume. We are grateful to Mrs Kathryn Chalaby-Amsler for her efficient work before and during the Conference and in the preparation of this publication.

INTRODUCTION

In November 1984 the Council for International Organizations of Medical Sciences (CIOMS), with the collaboration of the World Health Organization (WHO), convened a conference in Athens, Greece, entitled: "Health Policy, Ethics and Human Values — An International Dialogue".

The Conference explored the interaction of health policymaking, ethics and human values from several viewpoints. It focused on the model of the health policymaker, who must make decisions under pressure from a variety of social, economic, political and technological sources. It identified issues of importance to the participants' countries and led to increased understanding of one anothers' cultures and values. Especially, it resulted in an appreciation of the interdependencies of health policymakers, health-care professionals and ethicists in addressing these issues, and established common ground for continued collaborative exploration of the issues involved.

The present Conference was organized to consider these issues as they affect the industrialized countries of the world, mainly in Europe and North America. It provided a forum for an international dialogue on the applications of ethics and human values to health policymaking in those countries. Its purpose was to make explicit the principal ethical and human-values issues of relevance to policymaking in health matters, and to indicate the measures needed to ensure equity and social justice in the provision of health care, in the industrialized countries. At the same time, it provided for these issues to be considered in relation to the effects of health policies of industrialized countries on developing countries.

The programme was structured around four areas which typify the ethical and human-values issues that confront health policymakers: **screening and counselling**, with special reference to genetic engineering and interventions; **organ transplantation**, including patients' and donors' perspectives; **the elderly**, with regard to limits of care and quality of life and aging; and **lifestyles and health hazards**, mainly the issue of balance between individual choices and collective interests.

The last decade has seen enormous progress in biomedicine but even the richest countries have been faced with scarcity of resources and the need to reallocate them, and this has raised new ethical issues. These are critical ethical issues and they cannot be ignored in discussions on the interaction of ethics and health policymaking. Policymakers accept the validity of ethical considerations in health policy planning but want to know how ethics and policymaking may be joined, in the interests of the public generally and of patients in particular, and especially in the interests of the underprivileged and underrepresented sectors of the population. The Conference in bringing together health policymakers, ethicists and biomedical experts permitted such issues to be investigated and their resolutions explored.

Health policymakers initiated the dialogue by asking how recent technological advances in medicine may be reconciled with the norms of ethics, human values and socio-economic reality, particularly those advances that have triggered considerable ethical debate.

Physicians and nurses had the opportunity to offer their views on the interaction of medical advances with health policymaking (macro-ethical aspects), and on the implications of new clinical technologies for service to patients (micro-ethical aspects).

Ethicists assessed both the macro-ethical and the micro-ethical aspects of these biomedical developments. They took into account the norms and values of different cultures, as well as differences in norms and values across geographical and cultural boundaries. They considered also recent efforts to introduce new normative concepts into biomedicine, such as quality of life, and new advisory mechanisms, such as hospital ethical review committees.

Finally, health policymakers were able to discuss the extent to which such dialogue helps them in defining the limits of health care and in making decisions which promote the interests of the public and of patients. Thus it may be said that the Conference contributed to a better understanding of the implications for health policymaking of the ethical debate about genetics, organ transplantation, the care of the aged and health hazards.

This book has two main sections — the Highlights of the Conference, a synthesis of the principal concepts and issues which emerged from the presentations and discussions, prepared by Dr J.H. Bryant, and the proceedings, consisting of all the background papers presented and the reports of the discussion groups at the Conference.

Z. Bankowski, M.D.
Executive Secretary, CIOMS

INAUGURAL CEREMONY

The President of the Council for International Organizations of Medical Sciences (CIOMS), Professor Francisco Vilardell, opened the Conference in the presence of His Royal Highness Prince Claus of the Netherlands in Noordwijk aan Zee at 11:00 a.m. on 2 June 1987 in the Grand Hotel Huis ter Duin.

Dr J. van Londen
Director-General of Health, Ministry of Welfare, Health and Cultural Affairs, Rijswijk, the Netherlands

Your Royal Highness, Mr Chairman, Your Excellencies, Ladies and Gentlemen. First of all I have to apologize for the inability of the State Secretary, Mr Dees, to come here this morning. He is involved, as many of you living in the Netherlands know, in all sorts of activities occurring now in the health field. I shall read his speech to you.

It is a great privilege and pleasure for me to welcome you on behalf of the Netherlands Government. We are greatly honoured by the presence in our midst of His Royal Highness Prince Claus of the Netherlands, whose great interest in ethical and scientific matters is well known. We are grateful indeed that it was possible for him to be with us here today. As a side remark, I would note his presence not only as a member of our Royal Family, but also as the Chairman of the Foundation for Public Education and Information about Science and Technology, and it cannot be seen separately from his role as a co-founder and now Honorary Chairman of the Foundation for Biosciences and Society, whose aims are so closely connected with those of this conference.

First of all I want to congratulate Dr Vilardell on his election as President of CIOMS.

I have pleasure in welcoming Dr Dunne, representative of WHO headquarters, Geneva, as well as Ms Pinet, of the Regional Office for Europe of the World Health Organization in Copenhagen.

I should also like to welcome Professor de Wied, President of the Royal Netherlands Academy of Arts and Sciences, and the Burgmaster of Noordwijk, Mr Bonnike.

Lastly, I am glad to have the opportunity to extend my greetings to some representatives of the Netherlands Parliament. The Netherlands Government considers it a great honour to have a conference on "Health Policy, Ethics and Human Values" held in our country. The subject is an emotional one and also a highly political one, yet there are few subjects that require a more cautious approach. We are all aware of this.

If ethics is the art of asking the right questions, politics should be the art of giving the right answers. Merging the two would give politics an extra dimension. How lucky we are to have medicine in our midst today, for is not medicine a combination of both — asking the right questions, making the diagnosis, and giving the right answers! This is therapy, and therapy taking into account human values. The multitude of questions that beset us when we come to think of it is only matched by their magnitude. We seem to be overtaken, overwhelmed, by the developments. We in the Western World are dealing with advanced medical care and an ever-expanding medical technology. These questions of medical technology bring us to the boundaries of care, to the limits of care, and we might even say the frontiers of care. Man, in our society, seems to wish to push further and further. A recent television programme here in the Netherlands was called "Playing God". Humility seems to have left us. I would not be so one-sided as to link ethical questions only to medical technology. That would be putting matters in a wrong way. Matters of life and death do exist outside the development of medical technology, although the medical technology seems to be all the time in the background. Sometimes ethical solutions are found first and legal solutions afterwards. At other times, legal solutions emerge first, as it is the judge who is forced to take a decision. The ethicists might contribute to it, so that the decision will have been the right one, not only legally but also morally.

It is a felicitous moment to find members of the scientific and political community present here from all over the world. We are all aware of the fact that in different parts of the world different developments take place. Some societies deal with their problems differently from other societies. The tradition of litigation to settle ethical issues as seen in some countries might be one way to get minor details settled, but one wonders at what a price to the parties involved these solutions are being found. I am sure, however, that not solving questions and procrastinating are under the circumstances not very helpful either. We are here to learn from each other's views, to learn from each other's solutions, and to learn from each other's procedures, which help us to arrive at the solution of such difficult questions.

It is very useful that this conference has been convened by the Council for International Organizations of Medical Sciences. The number and scope of ethical questions is ever increasing, at both the macro- and the micro-level. Many of the questions at the micro-level entail decisions at the macro-level. Problems seem to be intertwined.

I should like to take the opportunity to say a few words about each of the subjects your conference is going to tackle.

Screening and counselling is your first subject. The term "foreseeable future" is the one that is most relevant for screening. We should like to see what lies ahead of a person and we are afraid that by knowing the future the term "foreseeable future" gets a different meaning and, as some think, a sinister one. What frightens people is that some might abuse this knowledge about the future. I give an example: If a certain risk condition is present or when it is sure that a person at a later stage in his life will get a disease, should we punish him for it? Can a prospective employer say "No" to such a person? Can an insurance company refuse this prospective client? Or should society set standards, either voluntary among the parties concerned or through legislation, to ensure that this

2

will not happen? Can we either forbid such questions from being asked, or set up a fund to deal in solidarity with their financial consequences? I know that this medal has a reverse side. A person who knows he has a deadly disease should not be allowed to profit from this fact, by, for instance, taking out a high life-insurance, but let us not dwell on examples.

Your next subject is organ transplantation. As we all know, there is a macro-dimension to this question, which could be called "the supply side" — how to organize enough donors, or organs. Also, there is a micro-dimension — who is to get the transplant? Political debate is vivid, as was illustrated again recently in our country. Our Scientific Health Council advised a change from a system of informed consent to a system of presumed consent, but this advice was unacceptable politically. Human-rights issues stir a lot of debate.

The elderly are not only a focus of your conference but also a focus in today's politics. It has often been said that civilizations can be measured by seeing how they treat their elderly. The better the treatment, the more civilized that society is. There is nothing worse, and not only from an ethical standpoint, than to see the elderly as a burden to society. There is still a lot to be learnt from communities outside the Western world in this respect. It would be useful if the conference could come up with some ideas on how to deal with this problem — not the problem of the elderly but the problem of the cultural treatment they get.

The fourth subject you are going to deal with is lifestyles and health hazards. As I see it, the subjects in this conference are interconnected. Most medical care is for the elderly and is for diseases presumably linked to lifestyles. Doctors sometimes feel ill at ease with these problems. They do not seem to belong to the domain of medical science — they sometimes even escape the power of the ministry of health — and yet intersectoral action is all-important, as WHO has justifiably been stressing over the past years. Questions of self-determination and influence of the state on its citizens have strong moral overtones. Shouldn't we then also come to grips ethically with the problems involved?

This brings me to the role of the state in these matters. It is my opinion that the state should create conditions under which ethical issues receive due consideration, at both the macro- and the micro-level. It is also the state's role to design policy and to take political decisions in ethical matters. This will undoubtedly mean legislation in many cases, but it should be borne in mind that it is of utmost importance that everybody can play his proper role in society, and I stress the word "society" here. It has this beautiful Latin root of *socius*, which I will translate as "mate" or "fellow". It even reminds me, with a few letters transposed in the word "mate", of the word "team", which seems to carry the same meaning. The German word *Gemeinschaft*, implying a common goal and doing things together, expresses it equally well.

Ladies and Gentlemen, the Netherlands are notorious for being a country of preachers, merchants and missionaries, and today I have to add — the weather, the bad weather. It was the German, Otto Heiner, who once maintained that everything in Holland happens years after it happened everywhere else. Maybe Heiner was right, but not in all respects, exactly because of the necessity of public discussion about the ethical problems with which progress of medical science will confront society and therefore politics and the state. The Foundation for Biosciences and Society was already established in the Netherlands in 1969. The initiative was taken by you, Your Royal Highness, together with your wife, our Queen, and some prominent politicians and scientists in those years. I think that in no other country does such a Foundation exist, with as its sole goal to present to as large an audience as possible the possible consequences to society of developments in the biosciences, and this through critical-minded information and education. If such a Foundation does exist elsewhere, I hope it will have been there for 18 years, as in our case. For 18 years the Foundation felt itself as a voice crying in the wilderness, as it had to work with limited resources it had to beg for. For in the euphoria of our Western thinking and belief in progress we fail to weigh the consequences of this very belief, which means we do not spend money on reflection. Yet, carrying on undauntedly and churning up a scrupulous awareness has gradually created a climate wherein the eyes of many are opened — too late possibly for developments that were to be foreseen in the distant future and now really at our doorstep. And sometimes we find ourselves in the middle of them.

When you, Your Royal Highness, in November last year, then still as Chairman of the Foundation for Biosciences and Society, held a lecture at the symposium in Amsterdam entitled "Biosociety", you said: "The Foundation for Biosciences and Society wants not only to have the function of informing the people in our society about what is going on in biosciences but also to have the function of informing bioscientists of what is going on in society." Don't we have — and I should like to open the conference in the light of this question — don't we have an infinitely greater need in our Western societies for more love and humaneness?

I wish you a fruitful conference and a pleasant stay. I thank you very much.

Dr John F. Dunne
World Health Organization, Geneva, Switzerland

Your Royal Highness, Your Excellencies, Ladies and Gentlemen.

It is an honour and privilege for me to extend to you greetings from Dr Mahler, the Director-General of the World Health Organization, and to address this conference on his behalf.

The Netherlands over the centuries has offered a rich contribution to the culture of this continent; it has made many discoveries vital to the development of the medical sciences and, through its staunch independence, it has played a vital role in shaping political institutions in

Europe. It has a proud history and an influence quite disproportionate to its size.

It is important that this conference also should exert an influence disproportionate to its size, firstly, of course, because of the issues it addresses. It is about the human face of medicine; about medicine in the service of the community; about how the resources and technologies now available can best be applied to provide most benefit to most people.

It is important, secondly, because in its conception it acknowledges that the associated problems, whether they are economic, social, ethical or cultural, are best defined and discussed through an interplay of ideas between those that shape policies, those that provide the services, and those that are concerned, from a philosophical or theological viewpoint, with the fabric of human values.

It is important, thirdly, because it can sensitize public and political awareness to the complexity and gravity of some of these problems. Even within the highly developed countries of Europe and North America, which are the primary focus of attention of this conference, the attainment of the World Health Assembly's aspiration of Health for All by the Year 2000 presents serious challenges to society. The abuse of tobacco and alcohol continues to take an unacceptable toll of health, life, productivity, family security and social services. The rapidly changing structure of populations in which the active work force is contracting significantly as a proportion of the population at large faces society with a need to support the disadvantaged, particularly the unemployed and elderly, dependent individuals in unprecedented numbers. And now, astride this already awesome social responsibility, rides the spectre of AIDS.

At the heart of this conference a disquiet is bound to emerge that many of the fundamental achievements that have been made in the biological sciences over the past decades simply cannot be widely applied in medicine, regardless of their ethical implications, as a result of lack of resources. The hope must be that this disquiet will stir some fundamental thinking and rethinking about the vital importance of health to the quality of life, not only for the individual but also for the well-being, integrity and efficiency of society at large. The year 2000 is almost upon us, and the challenge to health policymakers, and surely to governments, is undeniably intense.

WHO is not only grateful, it is highly indebted, to the Council for International Organizations of Medical Sciences for offering such an effective forum for discussing the social and ethical aspects of the many health-related issues that are now of acknowledged moment to the collectivity of its Member States. It cannot expect, of course, a set of effective solutions to devolve from any one conference, but it does regard this meeting as a particularly important event in CIOMS's broader programme of International Dialogue on Health Policy, Ethics and Human Values. The Organization is particularly appreciative of the collaboration, generosity and hospitality offered by the Netherlands Ministry of Welfare, Health and Cultural Affairs and the Netherlands

Institute for Bioethics, which have made this conference possible and which have, indeed, already prepared the ground so admirably for its success. I can assure you that the World Health Organization will pay due attention to the proceedings of this conference.

Ms G. Pinet
Regional Office for Europe of the World Health Organization, Copenhagen, Denmark.

Your Royal Highness, Dr Vilardell, Mr Executive Secretary of CIOMS, I have the honour today to represent at the opening of this conference Dr Asvall, Director of the Regional Office for Europe of the World Health Organization.

In the message he entrusted to me, he wants to thank you, Dr Bankowski, for your kind personal invitation to address this opening session. He wishes to underline the close relationship between CIOMS and the Regional Office and the very fruitful collaboration which ensues. His message also includes wishes for the full success of the conference, which go beyond the usual formalities. Dr Asvall's main preoccupation is to see that the health-for-all movement in Europe thrives. In this respect, he is convinced that because of the judicious choice of the topics to be discussed, which were recalled by Dr van Londen, this conference will be a valuable contribution towards our common goal of health for all. In particular, it will help to build up a consensus among the many different groups of people belonging to the disciplines related to health, many of which are represented here. Dr Asvall also recalls that the Regional Committee, two years ago, was hosted by the Netherlands and was marked by a special event — the first evaluation of our progress towards achieving health for all in Europe. This was an innovative undertaking which could not happen in a more appropriate place in view of the leading role played by the Dutch Ministry of Welfare, Health and Cultural Affairs in elaborating their national strategy for health for all.

Dr Asvall also wishes, in such an important public gathering as ours today, to render public homage to the remarkable skills with which Dr van Londen as its President conducted the last Fortieth World Health Assembly.

Personally, may I say how pleased I am to participate in your work. I feel particularly happy to visit again our host country.

The programme of your conference has already expressed very clearly the fact that the goal of health for all raises many questions with strong implications for health policy, ethics and human values, particularly those of equity and social justice. An international dialogue on these issues could not be more appropriate and timely. Since the health-for-all movement will be one of the dramatic frameworks of these discussions, let me recall some of its highlights in Europe.

The policy of health for all was perhaps thought to be made first for developing countries but it has proved now relevant to industrialized and affluent societies as well. Let us recall that in spite of the high level of development in our region, the technology, which has already been mentioned, the money invested, the progress in medicine — in spite of all these the health of the people of Europe has not improved as rapidly as might have been expected and, furthermore, preoccupying inequalities in health still exist. It was in this context that the European Office of the WHO began a broad participatory process in defining the health-for-all goal in the region. This new approach and original initiative led to the adoption by our Regional Committee in 1980 of a model health policy applicable to the region as a whole — the Regional Strategy for Health for All. After a four-year development period, in 1984 the Regional Committee went a significant step further, completing this strategy by the adoption of a series of clearly defined 38 targets. These were the first common public health objectives adopted at the level of the European Region. I am sure I shall have an opportunity to come back to these targets during our conference.

We have been accused of being more optimistic than realistic, but today there is a clear concept of what health for all means in European terms, and the Region has a clearly defined, forward-looking, realistic policy. However, knowledge alone is insufficient; there must be a will to achieve. Such will exists, as demonstrated by the full political support received at the regional and national levels for this policy. A large number of European countries have already taken very serious action to follow up the 1984 pledge. Different degrees of public commitment have been expressed in three-quarters of our member states. Our approach is broadly supported by many professional societies and non-governmental organizations. Support is also beginning to come, but more slowly, from university circles and other intergovernmental organizations in Europe. Knowledge and will are effective only to the degree that they are accompanied by action. Action, however, is dependent upon the capability of those implementing the health-for-all policy. To be able means not only providing the necessary resources but also finding the appropriate ways to carry out successfully such a development process for health. Obviously it is not an easy task to motivate the governments of a region covering 800 million people. This region — the European region — is also one of great cultural and political diversity, and therefore the tactics of implementation of our declared policy will have to be various and numerous. In many instances, new and imaginative proposals will have to be sought. Moreover, when ethical issues are taken into account, the matter becomes of considerable complexity and full of subtle difficulties.

It is therefore necessary that other forces join the effort in order that new perspectives be explored. This is where the particular abilities and experience of non-governmental organizations offer WHO such valuable support.

May I take this opportunity in the name of the Regional Office to thank CIOMS for its willingness to take up the health-for-all issue in the forthcoming debates of this conference. In your selection of ethics and human values as the dominant element in your endeavour to study interaction with health policies, you have chosen the most noble and elevated of all approaches. I am confident that the contribution of this meeting towards accelerating the development of health for all will be not only forward but also upward.

This puts a heavy responsibility on the shoulders of each of you during the working sessions ahead, and the Regional Office places great hope in the outcome of the conference as a significant milestone on the way to the European and North American goal of health for all.

Thank you.

Professor D. de Wied
President, Royal Netherlands Academy of Arts and Sciences,
Amsterdam, Netherlands.

Your Royal Highness, Mr President of the Council for International Organizations of Medical Sciences, Your Excellencies, participants of this workshop. On behalf of the Royal Netherlands Academy of Arts and Sciences, it is a great pleasure and an honour to welcome you here.

This conference on Health Policy, Ethics and Human Values brings ethicists, health policymakers, health professionals and politicians together and its intention is to function as an international forum on the application of ethics and human values to health policymaking. I trust that there are also a number of medical investigators present because they are not the least important link in the chain connecting fundamental research to health care technologies; at least, I think it justifies my presence here.

The subject is of great concern to our government, as you have already heard from Professor van Londen. The Royal Netherlands Academy of Arts and Sciences is engaged in technology assessment in the widest possible sense. On request of the Parliament the Minister of Education and Science took the initiative last year to create a national steering committee for technology assessment; the mission of this body is to make social and ethical consequences of technological achievements feasible. This steering committee operates under the auspices partly of the Royal Netherlands Academy of Arts and Sciences and partly of the Council of the Governmental Science Policy. Conclusions based on the steering committee's reports have to be explained to society by a public information body which was recently founded and of which, as you have heard, Prince Claus is Chairman. This was a logical choice because he, together with Her Majesty the Queen, [which has already been said also by Dr van Londen] took the initiative, now nearly 20 years ago, to establish an institution meant to inform the public on developments in and consequences of biomedical research. Their concern made many of us in biomedical research aware of the need to leave our ivory towers and tell the people about the possible consequences of our research. The government, however, evinced little interest in this activity and I still remember the very difficult discussions we had, the Prince and others involved, for getting money for these efforts over many years. I'm happy that now it is the time that really this kind of activity is being acknowledged and being funded by the government.

Now the Academy is an independent advisory body of the Dutch government in all matters of science. The members of the Academy are appointed solely on the basis of their scientific achievements. The seat of the Academy is in Amsterdam and it is a meeting-place for scientists at the national and international level. As such, the Academy is also the adhering body to various international organizations, such as the Council for International Organizations of Medical Sciences, under whose auspices this meeting is taking place.

The Academy has two divisions — a science division which consists of several sections and a division on humanities, also with a number of sections. It is supported in its advisory task by special councils and committees composed of members and non-members. An important committee is the one on medicine. The second main activity of the Academy is the management of research institutions, and amongst these are a number of outstanding biomedical institutes. Thus, I would say that there is more than enough expertise in the Academy also for the issues to be discussed at this conference.

Health for all is the aim of the World Health Organization. In the Western countries the introduction of new and expensive technologies might put this aim under pressure. This raises many questions for health policy, ethics and human values. It has been said already this morning, but I must repeat it again, that the people of the Netherlands consist of merchants and missionaries. Accordingly, the dialogue on the issues that you treat during this conference is of great interest to at least half of the people of this country.

I hope that this conference will be fruitful and inspiring to all of you. Thank you.

Mr J. M. Bonnike
Burgomaster of Noordwijk, Netherlands.

Your Royal Highness, Mr Chairman, Ladies and Gentlemen. On receiving an invitation to extend some words of welcome to your conference in my town, I felt inclined to take some words literally.

Looking over your programme, I counted about 22 hours of ceremonies, sessions, working groups and discussion within only four days. In order not to disturb your concentration on which heavy appeal is made, I should reduce my speech to a well-meant and hearty welcome to this excellent and fashionable seaside resort where you can even have your watch repaired on Sundays — isn't that true Mr Chairman?

Your selection of Noordwijk as conference town was a very wise one. As early as 400 BC, the Greek physician, Hippocrates, claimed that human behaviour and welfare were positively influenced by the sea

9

climate. Nowadays, the sciences of thalassotherapy and biometeorology state that the marine climate, the bracing air and the sea water do strongly influence the human health rhythmic phases in which we live. Moreover, they stimulate concentration and bright discussion. Therefore, reading your programme I miss a daily walk along the beach before breakfast, a healthy sea-bath before lunch and a walk through the dunes after dinner. Moreover, it's quite likely that you would then meet your compatriots in this international ambience. Anyway, I am sure that if you can spare time for all these healthful activities from this strenuous and, above all, important conference, you will return home healthier and happier than before.

May I wish you with all my heart a fruitful conference in the interests of the many people all over the world who need our help to achieve a happier and more humane life.

HIGHLIGHTS OF THE NOORDWIJK CONFERENCE

J. H. Bryant*

Background to the Conference

To appreciate the intent of this conference at Noordwijk, we need to go back to Athens and 1984, when the Council for International Organizations of Medical Sciences (CIOMS) and the World Health Organization (WHO) sponsored the first in this series of meetings on Health Policy, Ethics and Human Values.

The planning of that event began with appreciation of the role of the policymaker. Given a technological advance, whatever the biomedical content and the ethical implications, it is often at the policy level that the societal impact will be determined; and health policymakers usually form their decisions under pressure from a variety of social, economic, political, technological and ethical sources.

The Athens conference began, therefore, with the policymakers, and explored their interactions with health professionals and ethicists around specific health-policy dilemmas. The question was, could these three parties listen to one another, learn from one another about current problems, and then go on to new concepts and unexplored ground? The results far exceeded expectations, particularly in terms of how different cultural perspectives sharpened the debate, added new insights, and, in the end, brought better understanding of the differences.

Dr Edmund Pellegrino established the ground on which the Athens conference would do its work when he defined the major terms of its title:

The health policy of a nation or a community is its strategy for controlling and optimizing the social uses of its medical knowledge and resources;

Human values are the guides and justifications people use for choosing the goals, priorities and means that make up strategy;

Ethics acts as a bridge between health policy and values. Ethics examines the moral validity of the choices that must be made and seeks to resolve conflicts between values, which inevitably occur in making these choices.

He went on to point out three general purposes that motivate health policies:

* Professor, Department of Community Health Sciences, Aga Khan University, Karachi, Pakistan.

11

First, to attempt to control the social and economic impact of the unrestrained use of advanced medical technology in treating individual patients;

Second, to achieve a more equitable distribution of the benefits of medical knowledge;

Third, to use medical knowledge in an anticipatory way for the collective good of present and future generations.

Then, in one of the most perceptive remarks of the conference, Dr Pellegrino added:

Health policies are rarely derived from explicit and systematic analysis of the moral values that shape them. Much of the art of national and international policy making consists in structuring decision-making in such a way that value issues are not confronted. The aim is to keep peace between, and within, divergent belief systems. However, once framed, a health policy unerringly reveals the values that drive a society; and these cannot escape examination retrospectively.

Dr Robert Veatch focused his attention on the interactions between health policy and values. Health policymaking is always, and inescapably, an evaluative task. It is not only that value systems inevitably creep in to bias decision-makers, although they do. It is rather that policymaking logically requires a system of values. In large part these values are determined by culture.

He pointed out that value systems play at least four different roles:

First, value systems provide a framework for choosing among policy alternatives. It requires taking different feasible options and deciding which among them is the most valued pursuit, according to the ethical and other values of the group;

Second, value systems provide the framework for choosing who the policymakers will be. To choose the decision-maker is to choose the value system upon which decisions will be made;

Third, value systems are critical even in providing the medical and other facts upon which health policy decisions must be based. The cultural system of beliefs is critical for deciding which facts will be taken into account and how they will be used for purposes of policymaking;

Fourth, value systems are critical in determining what the possibilities are for intercultural cooperation in health.

The conference then, led by Dr Pellegrino's observations about the nature of health policymaking, and by Dr Veatch's insights into the place of values in policymaking, proceeded to examine some specific policy dilemmas. It had been planned, by agenda and membership, to explore how cultural and value differences interact with policymaking and related ethical thinking. 150 participants from more than 50 countries, representing a dozen cultural and religious groupings, brought a rich mixture of ideas, experiences and value systems.

It became apparent that different countries make different policy choices, but also that they see different questions as important according to their economic resources, patterns of disease, cultural traditions, and ethical and other value commitments. I will give a few examples of these differences.

The importance given to human life in a philosophical or religious sense is strikingly similar in many cultures, but the ways in which lives are seen, counted and cared for in real life very greatly. Human life is seen as of divine origin in the major religions, and even as having infinite value, but in villages and cities at the social periphery the question is asked: this infant who died of diarrhoea this morning — was it a person yet?

Care of the vulnerable and handicapped brings forward a number of conflicts between values given to life and the practical difficulties of day-to-day care. Ethics aside, much seems to rest on the willingness of a society to protect the vulnerable and absorb the handicapped, whether the handicap is that of having a cruel deformity, of being elderly and helpless, or of being born female.

Quality-of-life issues inevitably surface in relation to questions of resource allocation and treatment. What kind of life is worth preserving and who should decide that a life should be prolonged? In some countries, particularly the developed countries, these quesions are examined with great care, as they will be in this conference, and much is to be learned from the ways in which the questions are framed and answered. In developing countries, however, such questions often appear to be crushed under the immense burden of human need and the difficulty, even impossibility, of dealing with them. The subtleties that attract attention in the developed countries may not even be noticed.

Let me use an example from the subcontinent of India: the question of who should decide whether or not a woman is to have a Caesarian section for obstructed labour is influenced by family values, which often hold that the husband and mother-in-law (his mother) control decisions, but there may be no chance to ask this question because of the impossibility of getting the woman to a place where her life might be saved — the desert is too wide, the ox-cart too slow.

Here, the most meaningful questions are stripped of any ethical subtlety; they are plain policy questions: when will lifesaving health services reach these people?

Perhaps at no time during the conference were the differences among the values of its participants more apparent than when the discussion focused on the meanings given to life, suffering and death. Let me simply call attention to two statements that will give you indications of the range of the differences.

Avraham Steinberg reflecting on the religious values of Judaism about life, suffering and death said "Since the value of life is infinite and beyond measure, it follows that any part of life is of the same worth. One life is worth as much as a thousand lives — infinity is not increased by multiplying it. Man is obliged not only to sustain life by all means, but also to cherish it and preserve it in good health".

Pinit Ratanakul provided a Buddhist perspective: Death is not a one-time event; it occurs every moment of life. Birth and death are always present in juxtaposition to each other. Through an understanding of death we gain an understanding of life, and through finding the meaning of life we define the meaning of death. Life and death are two inseparable aspects of one entity. Life is like a dream — brief and fleeting.

With respect to the state of inquiry into bioethical issues in the Third World, it is probably fair to say that it is relatively early in its development, at least in terms of the questions and approaches being used in the North. There is a paradox here, since the culture and values of the South and East are as old as history itself. But there is an interest and a readiness to pick up the inquiry. Certainly we would all stand to benefit from their examination of the ideas that will be discussed here this week; and we would be keenly interested to see how they choose to modify the questions and frame the answers in the light of their own concerns and values.

This line of thinking led to an important outcome of the Athens conference, which was that the participants urged CIOMS to take the lead in facilitating an expanded dialogue around these issues, so that other countries and other parties might contribute to and benefit from such explorations.

CIOMS responded by establishing a new programme, called An International Dialogue on Health Policy, Ethics and Human Values. The CIOMS Office in Geneva serves as the focal point and ensures that the concerns of WHO are kept in the forefront. The International Dialogue has the following purposes:

to strengthen national capacities for addressing and making decisions about the ethical and human-values issues involved in health policy;

to contribute to improved understanding of WHO's goal of health for all, particularly its value content;

to develop transcultural and transdisciplinary approaches to working in this field;

to use these approaches as ways to pursue deeper understanding of human values across cultural and political lines.

A Steering Committee has been established and is currently formulating a set of guidelines for further discussions. It is expected that this conference will help to shape the directions that the International Dialogue will take.

The agenda of this, the Noordwijk Conference, so well planned by our hosts from the Netherlands and their CIOMS colleagues, is built around some of the most vexing health policy issues of our time. Its basis in European and North American perspectives does not lessen its relevance for the rest of the world, including Third World countries.

Indeed, we shall see that some of the policy questions being asked today in the North, such as new ethical questions raised by technological advances, will be faced tomorrow in the South. But we shall also see policy decisions lately forced on the North, such as the retreat from universal access to services for the elderly, imposed by rising costs and economic stringency, with which the South is already living.

Setting the Scene

A conference develops a life of its own, dependent to a considerable extent, but not entirely, on the plans and set presentations of the organizers. However, the most interesting, and possibly most important, aspects of a conference come as surprises — ideas, interactions, emphases, collisions, synergisms, conversions, turns of phrase, proposals and new-found interests of the participants.

So it was at Noordwijk as 150 participants from 35 countries came together into a conference place and plan arranged by CIOMS, WHO and the Netherlands Government. The independent life of the conference began to form even as the participants arrived at Noordwijk and continued as their interactions intensified during the course of the conference.

These reflections on the conference can capture only some of the major statements, ideas and proposals, certainly not all that is contained in the full presentations included in the body of the Proceedings. Nonetheless, here is a sample, drawn from the agenda of the conference and the interactions of its members, as they began by identifying familiar territory of health policy problems and ethical concepts, and then moved on to less familiar ground, raising new questions, probing for fresh insights, reaching for new, even partial, answers.

A Philosopher Focuses on the Interactions of Ethics and Policymaking

The stage was set for our deliberations by Professor Gorovitz, who provided a perfect illustration of the ethicist acting in relation to the policymaker. He outlined eight policy problems, each with important ethical content, which together showed the range of difficulties encountered, at least in the United States, in trying to generalize about interactions of health policies and ethics.

Let us recall some of them:

The problem of setting policies relating to abortion. There has not been a stable policy in the U.S. in relation to abortion. A bitter and divisive debate has ensued, and part of the population has actively opposed the policy. Here is an example of inevitable policy failure, not because the policy is necessarily wrong, but rather because any other policy on abortion would also fail. There is no common ground in the nation for a stable, incontrovertible policy.

The problem of policy relating to in vitro *fertilization (IVF).* The U.S. Government established a moratorium on funding of research on IVF. An Ethics Advisory Board reviewed the issues and recommended that the moratorium be lifted. However, this was seen as a politically sensitive issue and the Government continued the moratorium. To date funds are not available for research in this area, and IVF continues in the private sector — expensive, un-guided, uncertain. Here is an example of a lack of policy in the midst of moral controversy and political cowardice.

A policy prohibiting the sale of kidneys for transplantation. In the early 1980s, reasons were put forward to defend the sale of kidneys in relation to renal transplantation. Opposition to this was strong and consistent. The 1984 Organ Transplantation Act made it a Federal offence to engage in commercial marketing of kidneys or other human organs for the purposes of transplantation. Here is an example of a stable, widely supported and incontrovertible policy.

National policies relating to health care of the elderly. An example is presented of a 94-year-old woman who was hospitalized for 14 months with an accumulated bill of more than $500,000. She was unable to get better but was not getting worse. This was quietly terrifying the hospital administration. Should there be a limitation of access to health care by the very old and very sick? Or, do the elderly have a fundamental right to health care that must not be diminished by the fact of their age? Here is an example of a lack of policy where the need for guidance is rising by the day.

Policies in relation to AIDS. Here is a confusing landscape of health policymaking. There are diverse problems with no single forum or channel available for resolving the differences. Even within the Federal administration there are clear differences of opinion — for example, on the place and type of health education that should be directed towards children.

Other illustrations could be drawn from the presentation of Professor Gorovitz, but these indicate how he previewed many of the issues that were to be discussed during the conference, and focused our attention on the importance of keeping before us both their ethical and their policymaking aspects.

A Policy-Maker Speaks Out for the Humanization of Medicine and Health Care

Dr Eeva Kuuskoski-Vikatmaa, Member of Parliament and former Minister of Health of Finland, began by quoting the ethicist Martti Lindqvist:

> Even the best of institutions is not capable of listening, empathy, embracing or loving. This can only be done by people.
>
> M. Lindqvist

17

She went on to say that these words written by Martti Lindqvist crystallized the essence of health care: Man is at stake; we are to cherish his or her life and health, and not only treat cases or prevent disease.

This emphasizes the ethical basis for health policy. The core of ethics implies the informal personal values guiding man's actions and solutions. It does not mean fixed rules, official regulations, dictation or coercion. Ethics can only be based on free deliberation and personal responsibility.

On the one hand, the basic values of bioethics descend from the humanistic tradition, which emphasizes the uniqueness, subjectivity, interaction, freedom and integrity of man and joint responsiblity. On the other hand, the development of science and technology has brought forth the technical skills and many functions of modern medicine and health care. It has emphasized efficiency, specialization, skill in the use of instruments, dexterity and objectivity. Many ethical problems arise out of the tension between these different viewpoints.

The most important question of everyday health care is a continuous and confidential therapeutic relationship. This basis of healing and treating has, unfortunately, been pushed to the background in the euphoria generated by the advance of science of technology. We have created the illusion that technological equipment and new methods of treatment can replace this mutual and personal interaction between human beings. Basic care and human presence can be provided by any neighbour without specialist training. Open-care systems can be developed so that they provide the necessary and complementary support and assistance to the care given by the natural communities, in terminal care for example.

The extent to which it is possible to realize these ideas in daily life depends largely on the functioning of the popular movements, basic communities and voluntary organizations within each society. These bodies express faith in life, cooperational capacities and initiative of the citizens. Lack of such initiative is a sign of serious disturbance in the relations of the people with one another and with their futures.

From the point of view of human values, the spreading of increasing competition within the health care system has to be strongly opposed. In bioethics human beings must not be classified into successful and unsuccessful categories, guilty ones, and innocent ones. There can be nothing worse than morally labelling human beings on the ground of their diseases. Today it is possible and indeed necessary to examine ethical questions not only as ethics of care, but much more extensively as the ethics of health policy and biotechnology as a whole. The intention is not to undervalue moral and ethical aspects at the individual level, but rather to view them within a wider frame of reference.

In the promotion of the health of citizens, the traditional measures of health care are important, but also many other fields of societal life must be taken into consideration, such as lifestyles, nutrition, excessive use of alcohol and tobacco, traffic accidents and health risks in the environment.

Thus, Dr Kuuskoski-Vikatmaa speaks out for the personalization and humanization of medicine and health care, and against the over-technologizing, bureaucratizing, and commercializing influences of medicine. One is struck by the applicability of these principles, enunciated by a health policymaker from Finland, where health services and health status are among the most advanced in the world, to the poorest countries and poorest communities of the world.

> Here is a call for preserving the continuous and confidential nature of the therapeutic relationship, and its being situated within the supporting functions of the natural community. The viability of such arrangements depends largely on the strength of voluntary movements, community organizations and citizen initiative.
>
> E. Kuuskoski-Vikatmaa

Themes of the Conference

Screening and Counselling — a Paradigm for the Interaction of Biomedical Technology, Ethics and Policymaking

The papers presented by Professors de Wachter, Niermeijer and colleagues were carefully prepared, professionally presented and thoroughly instructive.

This seems the perfect paradigm for the theme of our conference: the science base is rigorously derived; supportive relationships with the patient population and their families are solidly built; linkages with the ethical implications of the technology of genetic screening are clearly constructed; these principles and perspectives are set in a broad world framework that is sensitive to the differences in their appreciation and application in other cultures; and there is careful constraint — do not do all that it is technically possible to do, but do only what is wise, prudent and responsible.

Two examples they provided of the possibilities and dilemmas raised by genetic screening and counselling can be briefly reviewed, one having to do with the ownership of genetic information, the other with uses and cautions associated with genetic counselling and genetic engineering.

Who owns genetic information? The moral argument on the matter of confidentiality has begun to move away from the traditional viewpoint that professional secrecy is in both the patient's and the doctor's interests. The first wedge driven into this position concerns the availability of genetic information to the relatives of the patient. If the health and well-being of the relatives are at issue, does the obligation to keep a secret then turn into an obligation to tell?

Another set of arguments supporting the communication of genetic information challenges the traditional notions of privacy and bodily integrity. In the past, it seemed as though the limits of my body coincided with the territory of my own privileged knowledge. Genetic medicine is clearly exploding such a view into a wider concept of corporate ownership of familial and ethnic autonomy. It now seems that the totality of my physical existence exceeds the limits of my body — genetic information should coincide with one's genetic extension, and consequently the traditional right to secrecy may turn into a duty to share information. Or, to put it another way, the previous non-existent right to know about others that which might affect me could very well turn into a new right to know.

Since genetic information may trigger highly emotional reactions, there is also an acknowledged *right not to know*. There are several reasons for wanting not to know. One reason has to do with the accuracy of screening tests, wherein false positives would give inaccurate

20

predictions. A second is that some people are unable to cope with the burden of the knowledge. Third, there is the possibility of misuse of information gained from predictive testing.

> The probable increase of predictive testing raises the issue of whether the *right* to receive information also contains a *duty* to receive information about the future prospect of one's life, since what one does with one's own life inevitably affects the lives of others.
>
> M.A.M. de Wachter

This notion raises provocative questions in relation to, say, those who might carry the Huntington gene: Is there a right to know? Is there a right not to know? Is there a duty to know?

A fundamental principle of patient autonomy would seem to be that it is a person's basic right to be or not to be tested, and to choose to be informed fully or only in part. Here, then, is an area of interaction between developments in biomedical science, ethics and health policy-making that needs further elaboration — the fundamental principle of the ownership of genetic information.

What uses and cautions should be exercised with respect to genetic screening and engineering? Among those in the medical genetics profession, there is no real concern that many people will ask for termination of a pregnancy because of the risk of a 'non-serious' medical condition. Both geneticists and the public should be clear about it: prenatal diagnosis, as one of the options in genetic counselling, does not lead to a 'handicap free' society. Even at maximum utilization of prenatal diagnosis and related action steps, there would not be a significant reduction in the percentage of congenital handicaps and diseases.

There is increasing awareness in the medical profession that predictive screening is warranted only if a free and informed decision is possible and also if adequate facilities and experience are available for long-term follow-up of those identified as disease-gene carriers at an early age. Another reason for concern is the risk of social crippling through knowledge of genetic predisposition, brought about by social discrimination by employers or insurance companies, for instance.

Genetic engineering involves the introduction of normal genes into cells, tissues or the whole organism as a cure for a genetic disease. This is an immensely complex field, still early in its development, in which the steps towards safe and effective application will be very demanding.

Introducing a gene into the *germ line* is another matter; it may be found unfeasible to do safely and effectively. Exchanging a bad gene for its normal counterpart might require genetic engineering of the egg fertilized *in vitro*. A major reason for not interfering at the germ-line level would be lack of understanding about gene function and regulation. It has been argued that the new genetic technologies could be used to improve the health of individuals, but also could change genetic make-up by adding to or deleting from the germ line some positive or negative genetic traits. Apart from the technical impossibilies and impracticalities, there are other reasons for not wanting to do this. To begin with, it would be impossible to define 'positive' and 'negative' traits. Even if it were possible, influencing the balance of human variation seems more dangerous than beneficial, considering that man has survived as a species precisely because of his variability and adaptive capabilities.

Moreover, even if it were possible to reduce the genetic transmission of a certain mutation, this would not generally eliminate the corresponding disease, because new causes arise through new mutations. It needs to be understood as well that much of the meaning of human variation is not in the genetic code but at the level of proteins and (behavioural) phenotypes. This realization will help to preserve the proper perspective in any consideration of the 4000 genetic disorders, occurring in and among the 50,000 structural genes, apparently essential to keep a human being and his society going.

In addition to such a rich coverage of current issues in this field, this group identified areas of further concern to this scientific community:

- the possibilities and difficulties of undertaking somatic gene therapy
- the extreme scepticism and cautions to be maintained in considering germ line embryo therapy
- the social risks associated with occupational screening for genetic susceptibility to hazards in the work-place
- avoidance of prenatal diagnosis for sex determination and diagnosis of non-serious medical problems or even late-onset diseases

They specified areas that call for further development:

- the ethics of the uses of amniocentesis and chorionic villus biopsy for determination of sex of the fetus, and diagnosis of late-onset diseases (such as Huntington's chorea), and of treatable diseases (such as phenylketonuria), and considering abortion as one of the therapeutic options.
- cost-benefit analysis as it relates to genetic screening as applied to such issues as the quality *vs.* longevity of human life.

Impression

The interaction of science, ethics and policy-making in this arena of genetic screening and counselling has reached a very mature stage:

- areas of scientific and ethical uncertainty are largely subject to extension of current experience and established methodology.

- relationships with policy-makers are well established, so that as advances in this field open up new questions in ethics and related policymaking the dialogue with policymakers is readily undertaken.

- here is an excellent resource for other countries which are less advanced but which are beginning to face some of the same questions.

Transplant Policies

European and North American Perspectives

The background material made available to us by Professors van der Werff and Vilardell was meticulously prepared and provided us with a clear view of a rapidly changing field in which scientific, ethical and public-policy issues are in great flux. They went well beyond the presentation of generally accepted positions on ethics and policies to the actual formulation of recommendations, guided rigorously by ethical principles, that might be considered by various countries. While these materials and the reports from the discussion groups were rich in detail, the commentary here focuses on a few of the highlights.

Among the many possibilities of transplantations of organs and tissues, they chose to deal with those relating to kidney, heart and liver. Improvements in the survival prospects of patients with these transplants, due to major advances in surgical and immunosuppressive technologies, have transformed the policy and related ethical issues in this field. Renal transplantation has better survival expectations than renal dialysis, and one-year patient survival rates for heart transplantation exceed 80% and for liver 60%.

> The combination of the life-saving power of organ transplant and associated technologies with problems of cost and organ scarcity creates a dramatic policymaking environment, including the most fundamental of ethical questions.
>
> F. Vilardell
> A. van der Werff

Looking ahead to the turn of the century, advances in technology and changing resource constraints provide strong indications that the future cannot be ignored in considering these difficult issues.

In considering transplant policies, a number of determinants must be kept in view:

23

Ethical values. Policy development in organ transplantation should largely be directed towards saving lives and improving the quality of life. The Hastings Center report on this subject recommended that policies should not only contribute to an increase in the number of cadaver organs obtained for transplant, but also acknowledge and advance the moral values and concerns our society has regarding individual autonomy and privacy, the importance of the family, the dignity of the body, and the value of social practices that enhance and strengthen altruism and our sense of community.

Religious traditions. While the Christian tradition no longer occupies an official regulative position in Western life and culture, it does remain highly influential. The Christian and Jewish emphasis on the "embodied self", rather than a sharp dualism of "spirit" and "body", involves a respect for bodies both before and after death, which sometimes leads to opposition to organ transplantation. Nonetheless, Judaism and Christianity generally support organ donation. As the authors note, in matters so fundamental as the donation of human organs, giving and receiving are better than routine taking and getting, and certainly to be preferred to buying and selling!

Policies for increasing the supply of organs. Several policy options exist for increasing the supply of organs, each with strong ethical implications:

Informed consent involves the expressed consent of the deceased or of family members to donating an organ.

Required request involves establishing a system in which hospitals are required to offer families the opportunity to donate organs.

Presumed consent grants health personnel the authority to remove organs from cadavers for transplantation whenever usable organs are available at the time of death, in the absence of objection from the deceased or family members.

Sale of organs for transplantation has generated considerable controversy, especially regarding the exploitation of donors or recipients, and the encouragement of donations from poor or unhealthy persons, but, overwhelmingly, policy decisions have opposed commercialization of organ procurement.

Tax credits might be seen as a way to narrow the gap between need and supply of organs, but among the serious objections are that it may be difficult to draw the line between tax credits and sale of organs, and that this approach would tend to benefit the rich and the better off, and not the poor.

Changes in attitudes of the public and of health professionals from fears and misconceptions on the part of the former, and lack of knowledge and understanding on the part of the latter, will be necessary if the numbers of organs available are to be increased substantially.

Organization of organ procurement on a scale that will increase the likelihood that donors and potential recipients will be matched in a timely and efficient manner is a goal sought in each of the multi-country regions.

Equity in organ transplantation. Organs for transplantation will be scarce for the foreseeable future, and it is therefore essential that criteria and procedures for patient selection be publicly stated and publicly defended.

Selection criteria should not be based on morally irrelevant characteristics, such as sex or race. There is general agreement in Europe and North America to use broad medical criteria to establish waiting lists, and then to use narrower medical criteria to determine who should actually receive the organ that becomes available.

Access and ability to pay have obvious importance in terms of both ethical and practical considerations. Given the high costs but undeniable life-saving results of organ transplantation, difficult choices have to made. In view of more general policies of cost containment in the health sector, it is not surprising that transplant programmes would be caught up in these economizing efforts. There is consensus in some countries that governments should not restrict organ transplantation on the basis of such cost containment policies; at the same time, there is agreement that transplants for saving the lives of a few should not be done at the cost of other forms of health care for many others who need it.

Legislation in relation to transplantation. There is considerable variation in legislation governing transplantation, some of which is current and progressive, and some out of date. Some countries have none. There needs to be a progressive approach to legislation in this field, and, where possible, harmonization of legislation, dealing with such issues as:

Living donors
Determination of time of death
Cadaver organ donations
Commercial trade in organs
Organization of organ procurement
Equity in organ transplantation
Certification of transplantation centres

Impression

These papers provide a careful analysis of the policy and ethical issues related to transplantation, including recommendations of the authors for policy formulation. Though not discussed in detail at the conference, it is obviously necessary that there be clear channels for policy dialogue, and it is most impressive that the Netherlands Government has sponsored this conference and expressed its interest in giving further policy consideration to the key issues raised.

While the field is being moved rapidly ahead by advances in technology, particularly in surgical and immunosuppressive methods, the complexities and difficulties inherent in the field should not be underestimated. For example:

Non-compliance by countries, institutions or people with the ethical principles outlined here is a real risk, but getting such recommendations established and functioning in some countries or organizations could represent an important contribution.

Cost factors are of immense importance. Availability of transplant technology creates demand that emerges from existing need — the waiting lists quickly appear when the technology is available. To then respond fully to such need would escalate costs beyond resources that would be available in the foreseeable future.

The Third World will be able to proceed only slowly in this field. While the surgical and immunosuppressive technologies are not insurmountable, the problems of organ procurement are substantial (they will rely on live donors for some time), and, as with other forms of high-technology medicine, the problems of access and equity in the availability of services will continue to be very large in the poorer nations. The discussions at the conference can be seen as an agenda of issues of health policy, ethics and human values in the field of organ transplantation for Third World leadership to consider.

Health Care of the Elderly

A New Frontier of Policy and Ethical Questions

From Daniel Callahan's presentation through the contributions of Sir Douglas Black and the working groups it was clear that "the elderly" represent a different set of issues from those of screening and of transplantation. With both screening and transplantation, the ethical and policy issues rise largely from a technological base and from the problems of sorting out the applications of the technology. As regards the elderly, the issues have much more to do with the nature of the elderly as a population group — how distinct are they as a subset of society? what are their entitlements? what social and economic burdens do they represent for society? what are reasonable expectations in terms of length and quality of life?

Daniel Callahan set the stage for the nature and scale of the discussion

26

when he said that the ethical problems of resource allocation for health care of the elderly would be as difficult as any we face in the health sector.

> Given the rising proportions of the elderly in the population and the increasingly effective and expensive technologies that will be applicable to them, we are at the edge of a new and endless frontier of ethical inquiry.
>
> D. Callahan

He used the situation in the U.S. as the basis for his discussion, but the questions are at least similar in Canada and Europe. The historical pattern in the U.S. is worth recounting:

In the 1960s and '70s, a concerted campaign was waged to change the public image of the aged from dependent and basically sick to a group that is heterogeneous, productive, and capable of making major contributions to society.

In those same years, the U.S. Congress passed legislation to ensure provision of basic health care for the elderly, and health care and general support for the elderly has continued to be both socially and politically popular.

Over the past few years, there have been, simultaneously, a rising concern about the ever-increasing costs of health care for the elderly, and a recognition that current services for the elderly are seriously deficient.

Among the concerns about allocation of health care resources for the elderly is a seeming disparity between government money going to the old and the young — a ratio of six to one — and recognition that the old benefit more than the young from advancing technologies.

The ethical issues emerge: Is there a need to ration health care for the elderly? Should rationing be on the basis of medical need or on that of age? Should the elderly give up their rights simply because of age? Should questions relating to termination of treatment be included in the larger questions of rationing care for the aged? Despite these pressing questions, there is great reluctance to engage in either legal or public debate on matters of rationing health care for the elderly, which reflects the strength of the underlying social and political values associated with the elderly.

These are not questions that will be easily resolved by debate over the moral, ethical or political issues. Rather, the questions will continue to grow in variety and complexity — Callahan's "endless frontier".

Sir Douglas Black addressed some of the problems raised by Dr Callahan. He offered a general principle:

> Both by virtue of natural justice and in recognition of their contributions to society, both past and continuing, elderly men and women should have the same entitlement as all other citizens to health care and to the protection of society.
>
> Sir Douglas Black

The working group asked the pertinent question: "Does it make any sense at all to be thinking of 'the elderly' as a single class?" The group answered with a recommendation to the effect that the obligations of the family and society towards the elderly can best be discharged if there is a clear recognition that the elderly do not constitute a single class, group or category. In their totality they are as varied as any other grouping of human beings such as children, farmers, or a particular social class.

Sir Douglas went on to emphasize that the rights of the elderly should not be put ahead of the rights of other members of the community; there should be no setting off of the elderly against children or against the working population, for these people also have got their societal rights.

Recognition of the individuality of old people is an important prerequisite for the proper satisfaction of their needs, one aspect of which is the very different wishes and expectations of elderly people themselves.

In the overall care of the elderly, medicine and even nursing have a relatively small part to play in comparison with the family and other social services. Medical advances, of course, can contribute to both prolongation of life and lessening of disability. These same advances also bring economic problems through their intrinsic cost, which, by the way, is due not only to high-technology medicine but also to inefficient uses of low-technology medicine, which Sir Douglas referred to as 'sloppy medicine'.

Sir Douglas also reported on the discussion of the working group on the elderly, in relation to resource allocation and euthanasia. His thinking is so clear on obviously complex topics that key ideas deserve to be recalled here.

Resource allocation: In this matter, the elderly are in competition with mothers and children, at the other end of life; and also with employed people, on whom the provision of resources depends. Any calculation based on the duration of a life preserved must clearly favour children; and if it is also 'loaded' to take into account the likely 'quality of life' during the added years, as proposed by Alan Williams of York University Institute of Health Economics, this bias will be increased. On the other hand, older citizens have contributed to society, both by their work and by their taxes, and society in equity owes them a return. A

28

purely pragmatic approach might tend to direct resources away from the elderly, but the ethical values of fairness and equity may partly correct this. When a global allocation of resources has been made for the elderly, the further distribution of such resources should depend in part on micro-economic analysis, e.g. to determine the balance between care in institutions and care in the community.

Euthanasia perhaps indicates rather clearly the ethical poverty of a purely pragmatic approach to problems of life and death. At its extreme, a pragmatic approach might replace retirement by extremes of deprivation, such as must have led to death in primitive societies, and may even contribute to it through malnutrition and hypothermia in what we call 'the developed world'. Even those to whom active euthanasia is anathema seem prepared to acknowledge that a life which has become extremely burden-some to the aged person need not be prolonged by what are described as 'unnatural means'. Even this concession raises considerable problems of .definition, e.g. what degree of pain or discomfort constitutes 'extreme burden'? And are 'unnatural means' limited to complex life-support systems, or do they include antibiotic treatment of life-threatening infection?

At the other extreme from those to whom active euthanasia is repugnant on moral or religious grounds, there are societies in which it is practised with some frequency, without the sanction of the law, but with the connivance of law-enforcement agencies. The very existence of these extremes of attitude would appear to bring it within a category of moral problem defined by Professor Gorovitz in relation to abortion. It is a situation in which no possible codification can conceivably satisfy the aspirations and also the consciences of all concerned. There is the possi-bility of a whole series of uneasy compromises between the extremes of total permissiveness and total prohibition; the choice among them will perhaps have to be decided by some form of 'situational ethics' rather than by undiluted deontology or utilitarianism.

> Who decides? In relation to resource alloca-tion, the deciders are primarily legislators as the elected agents of society, but legislators advised by doctors on what is possible, or by economists on what is available or what is economically the best bargain. Euthanasia is a much more difficult problem — legislators can only provide a framework, and indivi-dual decisions rest primarily with the patient, who is after all the possible victim of a conspiracy between doctors and relatives, when the protection of the law is less than absolute.
>
> Sir Douglas Black

Daniel Callahan's summary of the group discussion capped the consideration of the elderly in a far-ranging way. He divided the major issues into three groups: conceptual problems, moral dilemmas, and moral reforms — a classification that provides an organizational framework for understanding issues that could otherwise be confusing and murky.

The conceptual problems — with important moral and value implications.

Can one generalize about the elderly? Is it possible to generalize about the elderly while at the same time taking into account individual differences? Or could that very effort itself be harmful to the individuality and variety among the elderly? How does one avoid stereotyping the elderly? How does one avoid classifications that may be demeaning?

How do we want to define the old and the aged? Who are they? There are shifting ideas and policies on what constitutes retirement age. Distinctions are sometimes made between the young-old, the old-old, the frail-old, and the very old. Such classifications have a bearing on not only the way society understands the old but also how the old understand themselves — the old will understand themselves in great part in terms of the way society understands them.

What are the minimal levels of health care? First, what levels of health care are minimally necessary for all age groups, and then what for the elderly? This raises the further question: What is the relationship between health and aging? How do we relate health needs to our understanding and classification of the elderly?

Is aging a normal process? Of course it is a normal process, but given the possibility of biomedical intervention it is possible to consider that aging has the characteristics of disease. Whether it is defined as normal or not could determine one's opinion as to whether aging ought to be fought or accepted.

Can we define quality of life for the elderly? What would be the constituents of such a definition? How will need relate to quality of life? We can talk about medical need, or social need, but the effort to define need or quality introduces scientific and technical definitions that tend to be value-loaded.

How are we to understand the nature of the life cycle? At times we tend to use adulthood as the paradigm, and we see children as those who have not reached adulthood and the elderly as those who have passed adulthood. Should we understand the life-cycle in a richer way, not using one particular stage as the paradigm but rather

30

recognizing that each stage has its particular problems and benefits, opportunities and possibilities?

The moral issues and dilemmas — those issues where important values are pitted against each other, but it is unclear which is the appropriate choice:

Is there need for a theory of limits pertaining to health care for the elderly? Is it appropriate to talk about limits for the elderly as distinguished from limits of health care for other groups? Does not singling out the elderly for discussion of limits raise difficult questions about the way we understand and classify the elderly?

It is possible to define a proper balance of resources among and between generations? What is the right way to apportion resources between the young and the old?

How are we to find a proper balance between home care and institutional care for the elderly? This raises another question: the distribution of obligations. How are we to balance family obligations to take care of the elderly against governmental obligations?

Should priority be given to research that would extend life or that would improve the quality of life? Should we spend money on heart disease and cancer, which are killers, or on arthritis and other conditions that are not lethal but cause a great deal of suffering?

Euthanasia, a general moral dilemma. While euthanasia constitutes a moral dilemma very broadly for society, does it represent a special moral dilemma in the care of the aged and the way society values its elderly?

Moral reforms that are necessary. These do not appear to divide people or create agonizing choices, but nonetheless are important moral concerns.

Participation of the elderly in determining their own fate and welfare. They ought to be particularly represented in policy decision-making, and there should be advocacy groups for the aging.

Better care is needed for older women. Older women receive poor care, particularly in poor communities. This represents a distinct and unfair situation where strenuous corrective efforts should be undertaken.

There should be better integration of medical and other social and welfare services. Integration needs to be strengthened among health and other social services, among the various agencies working on behalf of the elderly, and among the professions and professional perspectives of those dealing with the elderly.

31

The need for new social roles for the elderly. There is great uncertainty in all our societies as to just what the elderly are supposed to be and to do. How might we redefine or clarify the present roles of the elderly?

The need to strengthen the family. If the family is to be a major source of care for the elderly, then the welfare and strength of the family is critical. In those countries where the extended family is still in place, all the more attention should go to preserving its protective and supportive role for the elderly.

Callahan closed by saying that in considering health care for the elderly, there have been such radical changes of late that we are now forced to re-think many things, beginning with the way we understand basic concepts and use terms and classify people. We are going to have to develop new values, devise better delivery systems, and engage in a number of experiments relating to the elderly and their health and health care.

Impression

Here is a field of biomedical and sociomedical science that is much earlier in its development and maturation than screening and transplantation. The medical, ethical and policy issues are just being discerned, and many of the key issues are not technologically based but rather linked directly with delivery systems and societal perceptions, and with value systems that shape these perceptions.

Paradoxically, while the elderly and their needs for health services have been with us all along, there are entirely new issues precipitated by demographic shifts, technological advances and related rising costs. These new issues create a fresh context in which the most fundamental ideas, terms and values must be re-examined. The strength of this discussion at the conference has been to go beyond reworking of old material to a clear and fresh design of new guidelines; and Callahan would quickly say that it will not be a one-time effort but a continuous one — a new and endless frontier.

The implications for the Third World are clear. There is no reason not to expect that the demographic patterns of the elderly of the Third World will evolve in the same direction as in the West, and that many of the ethical and moral concepts, dilemmas and reforms will be similar. The critical challenge to the Third World will be to address these issues in terms that are consistent with their own societal needs and values.

Lifestyles and Health

The introductions of Drs Monique Bégin and Edwin Fisher approached the field from entirely different directions, and each helped to shape the perspective developed by the conference on this intriguing and complex subject.

Monique Bégin's presentation was that of a policymaker with years of experience as a senior policymaker of government in both domestic and international situations. Hers is an assessment of the place of lifestyles in national health development. It is built on an unusual combination of social insight and political understanding, and serves in a perfect way the intent of the conference — to have policymakers lay out the practical, fired-in-reality, issues that must go into considerations of the ethical and value implications of health policymaking.

Edwin Fisher dealt with the social dynamics of interactions between the larger community and individuals who pursue lifestyles that are inherently harmful, and thereby represent burdens to both the individuals and the community. He raises questions about the balance of rights and responsibilities between the individuals and the community. He offers a perspective that is sensitive to the social origins of many of these problems; he carefully avoids blaming those who exhibit potentially harmful lifestyles, and calls for a social morality involving a caring interaction of community and individuals.

Together they suggest a field of inquiry that is very early in its development, where the key issues of concern are still being sorted out, where policy questions are being tested empirically, and where the ethical and human-values content is also in the early stages of identification and exploration.

Individual Choices and Collective Interests

Monique Bégin pointed out that despite policy pronouncements contained in the book "A New Perspective on the Health of Canadians" (1974), which gave attention to health promotion and prevention far in advance of other nations, these concepts remain the poor relation of the health system. Is it fair to conclude there has been a complete failure of health policymakers on this front? Why has good logic not worked? Is legislation an agent of social change? How could change be operated or engineered?

A rapid judgement on progress in the field of health promotion and disease prevention in Canada would indicate that some action has taken place:

Despite much debate about "infringing on personal freedom", legislation with fines has imposed the compulsory use of car seat-belts.

What is now called the "yuppy generation" is serving as an important private-sector market for the food industry (diet frozen foods of all sorts) and for the exercise industry (leisure, sports, health clubs, clothing). In North America, at least, market forces succeeded where health ministers and policymakers failed.

Some progress has taken place towards a "smoke free" society and, in Canada, for the first time, most people do not smoke.

The public is now well aware of water pollution and, in particular, of "acid rain" as major threats to the environment.

Some progress may have taken place in the image of health as inclusive of a healthy lifestyle. Personal responsibility for it is a completely different matter. Citizens live in an era of paradoxes when it comes to the co-existing sets of values promoted by society. Some examples:

The "me" society of the '60s, whose aim is the satisfaction of personal development, self-fulfilment, and individual needs and desires. It operates within the context of the consumer society, with a refusal to consider even intellectually the possibility of limits to growth, or even of limits to satisfaction.

The so-called counter-culture, on the other hand, which brings us back to nature and is best exemplified by the ecological movement. One of its spin-offs has been the holistic orientation — an integrated perspective for interpreting one's own needs and for dealing with the human being.

The faith in progress, which, in this century, takes the face of an absolute belief in science and technology as the new name for reason. Space exploration and the world of micro-chips are typical new cult objects. Whatever the uncertainty or doubt that pervades the applications of these technologies, citizens are not questioning the concept of progress.

These are the paradoxes individuals have to cope with in trying to decide what behaviour they are going to adopt, and for what reasons. Policymakers share the same uncertainties, plus a few of their own.

The internal logic of the biomedical model itself is a limitation, not to say a negation, of the importance of health promotion and disease prevention and healthy lifestyles. Medicine is no longer an art, but only a science, and therefore interested only in demonstrated causal relationships. Very few individuals question radically the validity of the biomedical, curative model. Some would like to see the humanization of medicine. Others want to enlarge the biomedical model in order that it would also encompass the so-called alternative medicines.

Given the budgetary limitations of the recession and the expectations of no-growth or limited-growth economies, policymakers and politicians alike know very well that existing budgets for curative medicine will under no circumstances be reduced, even infinitesimally, to give way to programmes promoting healthy lifestyles.

Can the discussion of the ethics of good lifestyles be placed in such a general societal context?

The notion of personal responsibility is somewhat diluted in complex, big governments characterized by the welfare state and extensive social "safety nets". A general "dependency syndrome" often co-exists with an acute sensitivity to unwarranted public spending. The sense that the person, the individual, can play a role is gone. Huge complex systems have taken over. Here is an erosion of the feeling of personal responsibility.

The concept remains one of personal, individual fate, not a concept of solidarity or of collective responsibility. It is most unusual to see public expression linking unacceptable lifestyles to an added burden to the costs of the health care system.

In Canada the one collective feeling that has emerged in the last ten years concerns the sense of protection needed by the environment. Yet, governments do not feel bound by this new attitude to the point of committing the budgets necessary to implement a policy of the environment.

> If biogenetic breakthroughs of these years have called for a new code of ethics, it is certainly not the case for the new definitions of what constitutes health: proper lifestyles. The focus of what health means remains centred on the biomedical intervention. It is equated with disease, illness, pain, handicap. Changes in one's behaviour rest at the periphery as something desirable, not as a powerful motive for action.
>
> M. Bégin

Community and Ethics in Lifestyle Changes

Edwin Fisher's remarks focus on the ethical issues that arise out of community efforts to promote health. The forces that promote risks to health extend throughout our societies, in our economies, our businesses, our public gatherings, our folkways, and our family and personal lives. To counter these forces, we must work throughout our societies, as caring and determined communities and as nations, to help all our citizens. Seeing ourselves as a community poses ethical problems. We fear both the loss of individual rights and the loss of community control of the individual.

Dr Fisher dealt with three ethical issues:

The interests of the group *vs.* the rights of the individual;

Individual *vs.* social responsibility for lifestyle;

35

Controlling diseases by focusing on disease entities *vs.* focusing on persons.

The interests of the group vs. the rights of the individual

When community and individual interests are in opposition, it is difficult to generate broad social affirmation of community health goals. This becomes clear in attempts to limit the right to smoke in public and in considering the right to privacy of results of AIDS testing.

Recent debate in the US Senate has focused on a measure that would require AIDS testing for marriage licences and not allow licences for those who tested positive. The restriction of the right to marry must surely figure as a substantial imposition of group interest on the interests of two individuals. Further, even the threat of such impositions is bound to undermine the willingness of those whose cooperation is necessary.

Individual responsibility vs. social responsibility for lifestyles

A central assumption of governance in many countries is the responsibility of individuals for the consequences of their behaviour. Thus, as the enormous consequences of lifestyles are recognized, there is a growing movement to hold individuals responsible. The growing movement to link health insurance rates with smoking status is an example.

> Given the commercial, social and biological forces that contribute to high-risk lifestyle behaviour, we must question policies that assume that such risks are freely chosen. We need to examine the ethics of policies which may punish members of our communities unfairly for habits or risks caused by diverse forces in our cultures.
>
> E. Fisher

Is there a fundamental conflict when society attempts to help people in need and at the same time punishes them for misguided habits through high taxes and insurance rates? Or, is it ethically permissible to promote better health through both help to improve lifestyles and disincentives to discourage harmful lifestyles?

Controlling the person vs. controlling the disease

Our confidence in mobilizing the community to endorse a behaviour change or a particular health habit may vary, depending on whether we take the perspective of dealing with those who have the health problems as persons or that of controlling the diseases as such.

The point here is that we wish to fight the disease, not the person with the disease. Public policy should be designed to combat tobacco smoking, not tobacco smokers.

36

In reflecting on these three ethical issues, we can see that mobilizing a sense of community to face challenges to our health raises important questions regarding the rights of the individual *vs.* those of society, the responsibilities of the individual *vs.* those of society, and the question of whether the integrity of the individual will be respected while combating the disease.

Two emphases may guide us in dealing with these issues. One is to emphasize the responsibility of all of us to assist and help those in need. The other is to maintain a respect for individuality and individual rights without unnecessary invasion of the lives of those we seek to help.

Impressions

As a field for inquiring into the interactions of health policy, ethics and human values, that concerned with lifestyles is even less well developed than that relating to the elderly. In dealing with the elderly, a key question was: how shall we define these issues? In dealing with lifestyles, the question seems to be: what are the issues that need to be defined?

The working group on lifestyles emerged with concerns that were puzzling in diversity, intricate in content, and important in social and political implications:

Are lifestyles determined voluntarily or otherwise?

Whatever the determinants, how can behavioural change be brought about? Can interventions be both effective in dealing with harmful behaviours and sensitive to individual needs and rights?

We need to have a better understanding of the biological, social, economic and political factors that facilitate or inhibit lifestyle changes.

The need to have ethical models that link personal freedom, individual responsibility, social responsibility and caring communities.

Recognition that there are many differences in lifestyles and cultures, as well as in the interventions to promote change.

A need for scientifically developed, empirically tested grounds for policies and initiatives.

A need for greater public access to information necessary to understand health risks and benefits related to lifestyle behaviours.

These issues — determinants, interventions, impacts — require very long-term perspectives.

Implications for the Third World are no less clear than for the West. The influences of lifestyles on health are pervasive in every society. How they are determined and how they are to be dealt with are tightly bound to local culture and circumstances. There is certainly no reason for Third

World countries to wait for solutions to these intricate problems to emerge from the West. While some insights into the problems will come from the more advanced countries, especially evidence for associations between particular lifestyles and disease entities, the Third World countries will have to develop their own social solutions and policy formulations, and these will be rooted in their own values and ethical precepts.

Reflections on the Conference

At the conclusion of the meetings and presentations of the working groups, a series of commentaries was invited from participants who represented various points of view:

> philosopher, policymaker, health professional, who represent the triad of disciplines which we bring together to engage in dialogue over these issues;
>
> philosopher and medical scientist from the developing world, to share their insights and to ensure that our debate is not isolated from the problems of the Third World;
>
> social scientist and biomedical scientist from Eastern Europe, to describe the experiences of their countries and to contribute to a balanced perspective from the West.

Excerpts are taken from their remarks.

The Viewpoint of the Ethicist

Sam Gorovitz said: total freedom is not an ideal; it is a contradiction. No one is free except in a social context of mutual rights, limitations and responsibilities. But what these responsibilities are and how they affect health policy is an exceedingly complex question.

In our four subject areas namely, screening and counselling, organ transplantation, the elderly and lifestyles and health hazards, we have seen the tension between individual and collective interests. What these areas have in common is that value questions are pervasive within them. They are not the sorts of question that can be answered in any stable and conclusive way. Ethical judgement is not independent of what is going on in the world. Indeed, it is about what is going on in the world; what goes on in the world of health care is ever-changing and the process of health policy formation is unending. There is a continuing need for ethical analysis as part of the basic process of health policymaking.

> In each of the four areas we have been considering, there are issues that can be resolved by remembering our traditional values of honesty, beneficence, respect for persons and justice. But equally issues arise that are new and that challenge our understanding of our own values.
>
> S. Gorovitz

39

Our traditional values do not suffice, even when they are clear, to answer many of the problems we face in health policy. One cannot look up organ donation in the index of the Bible. The Koran does not speak about the limits of genetic therapy. The works of Plato and Aristotle are silent on the use of life-extending therapies for the very ill and the very old.

Such sources may give us some guidance, but they always require, at the very least, interpretation and extrapolation, which are controversial, to achieve a satisfactory ethical analysis of a new problem in health policy. This is why it is futile to seek much specific ethical clarification in the context of a conference. Each specific issue requires separate specific enquiry, separate reflection and separate debate, and these take time and care.

The Viewpoint of the Health Policymaker

Dr Roscam Abbing said that taking proper account of arguments of bioethics is only possible if the ethics of policymaking itself is taken seriously. How is it possible for policymakers to be serious about bioethical arguments? There should be a continuous dialogue between policymakers and other parties, such as researchers, scientific workers in the ethical field, professionals in the health care field, and organizations of patients. All these parties must be addressed by government in a more systematic way than is the case at the moment.

> Government must scrutinize its own de-
> cision-making procedures in the light of
> ethics and must have the courage to ask for
> advice in matters that have a highly ethical
> content.
>
> E. W. Roscam Abbing

There are also other methods available to governments for promoting a more systematic approach to ethical questions, including the creation of research programmes in the ethical fields.

The Viewpoint of the Health Professional

Among his many interesting comments, Professor Doxiadis observed that the priorities reflected by the choice of topics for the conference did not reflect the priorities of the practice of health care. He felt that this gap in priorities was due to two causes:

The lure of technological progress: Teachers and researchers are eager to be among the first to exploit the possibilities afforded by

40

new knowledge and by new technology, and they often discard objectives which may be approached by old methods.

Many, especially academic, doctors fear "soft" data. They feel insecure. They prefer to ignore fields in which no "hard" data can be found, and to favour a rare disease because it can be approached through modern technology. Child abuse, for example, involves many ethical problems, but there is not a modern instrument to deal with it. Drug abuse is a similar problem. We must not neglect such problems just because they are the more difficult.

Professor Doxiadis concluded with:

One thing to avoid: groupings and generalizations about health conditions and problems, because there is such enormous variation among them.

One thing to respect: individuality.

Three needs to recognize:

— more risk assessment if we want ethical analysis.

— more auditing of our actions

— a clearer distinction between a difficult scientific choice and a difficult ethical choice, because we sometimes confuse the two.

He called for better medical training in the field of ethics, which in many countries is now where the teaching of psychology and social medicine was 20 years ago. He also observed that in these matters one must keep an open mind.

A Perspective of the Developing World

Pinit Ratanakul mentioned that in this meeting, and in many meetings in the West, discussions on ethics and human values usually are preoccupied with the value of justice and human rights, that is to say — what we must get from society. No one would dispute the importance of these ethical and human values.

> For the people of the East there is another human value that should be fostered both in health policymaking and in the practice of modern medicine. It is the ideal of compassion or loving kindness. It is a self-giving, self-denying, voluntary sacrifice of our own rights beyond what is socially obligated.
>
> P. Ratanakul

41

Medicine was born to give loving service to suffering humanity, but today these religious or human values are being lost and therefore must be fostered.

CIOMS must be commended for its plan to extend the International Dialogue to developing countries in order to make professionals and the public aware of ethical issues with which the West has struggled, particularly the uses of high technology in medicine. The developing countries will benefit from this dialogue, but they also have something to bring to the dialogue. The developing nations have a long cultural history and cultural resources which can be useful in seeking solutions to the new ethical problems we face in medicine.

CIOMS would do well also to promote transcultural research among countries so that we may find similarities and differences in human values and ethics among different nations, and at the same time some common human values that ought to be fostered in the promotion of health policies.

Ethical Considerations Driven by Economic Constraints in the Third World

Ben Osuntokun pointed out that the four themes of this conference, obviously of importance to the countries of the North, are also very relevant to the developing world of the South, though the priorities, methods, and technological and philosophical approaches to solving problems may differ.

> To ensure equity and social justice in the provision of health care it is now generally agreed that the best vehicle is primary health care, and it would be unrealistic for the developing countries to talk about health policies, ethics and human values without reference to primary health care.
>
> B. O. Osuntokun

With respect to screening and counselling, the main objectives must be early detection, treatment and prevention of disease and health promotion. In view of serious resource constraints in the developing countries, it is important to think of the feasibility of effective action and be guided by epidemiological patterns. An example would be screening for cervical cancer. It is obvious that screening coupled with effective intervention can reduce mortality due to cervical cancer. In most developed countries, screening covers ages 20 to 65 and is done every one to two years. Epidemiological data indicate that it would be nearly as effective, and more cost-effective, to screen those who are between 35 and 55 and to do so every ten years instead of every two.

In determining health policy, the feasibility of treatment and prevention as a result of screening is important. It is unethical to screen a population for high blood-pressure where as many as 20% may be hypertensive but where there are not the resources to treat those who require therapy. Experience in Nigeria has shown that those who do not know they are hypertensive prior to a screening programme will not comply with treatment, because of the side-effects of the drugs.

Screening for haemoglobinopathies, which are highly prevalent but about which little more can be done than counselling about the choice of a partner for marriage, is probably unethical. Screening for a disease which is rare and for which there is no effective treatment, or which appears late in life and cannot be treated, is unethical and unjustifiable.

Lifestyles? Alcohol abuse is increasing rapidly in some countries in the developing world, as are its somatic and mental consequences. So it is in Nigeria, where the medical cost of ill health caused by alcohol is much higher than the revenue collected from taxes on alcohol. The epidemic of tobacco-smoking disease has spread into the developing world with aggressive marketing by the tobacco companies, which has been described as the new slave trade.

It is ethical to take some statutory decisions, such as to control the advertising of tobacco products and to ban smoking from all public places and public transport. It is ethical and compatible with human values to mount vigorous health education programmes to encourage citizens to adopt healthy dietary habits. The developing world should be aware of the need to base health policies on medical and technological advances, and to do so in the interests of ensuring social justice and equity.

Perspective of an East European Country: Poland

Professor Sokolowska began with: "Your health in your hands!" While there are a number of interesting reasons for the emergence of this slogan, there are problems associated with the shift of responsibility for health promotion and protection from social institutions to the individual.

Sociological analysis suggests that the view of health as an individual responsibility tends to overestimate the magnitude of the health benefits that will accrue from changes in personal habits. This view tends to overlook or misconstrue the nature of the societal constraints on the individual will, and hence fails to specify the sociological conditions under which millions of individuals are able to change their lives significantly and the role social conditions have in maintaining unhealthy behaviour and attitudes. The focus on individual decision-making de-emphasizes the role of collective efforts on public policy in securing higher health standards.

> The notion of health as an individual respon-
> sibility underestimates the role of society in
> creating conditions under which indi-viduals
> both need and are able to mobilize their will-
> power. The only effective way to express our
> will is through collective action.
>
> M. Sokolowska

A Viewpoint from Eastern Europe: the German Democratic Republic

Professor Rapoport said that in 1983 the German Democratic Republic
(GDR) held a national conference on socialist lifestyle and health, and
there had been other symposia since on that subject. The view in the
GDR is that lifestyles are determined both by the conditions of life and
by the qualities and attitudes of individuals. Any improvement in health
must therefore encompass both the individual and society. Society has a
duty to guarantee health care, education and full employment.

> The emphasis on individual responsibility for
> the maintenance of health in no way reduces
> the responsibility of society to provide social
> security.
>
> S. M. Rapoport

As an example, there are the questions of whether a disease caused by the
person's own fault — overeating, alcoholism, drugs, negligence or ignorance — constitutes an abuse of the health system and should be covered
by health services, whether the coverage should include all types of
health-related expense such as that of dentures, eye-glasses, hearing-aids
and other prostheses, and whether all medicines should be free of charge.
The GDR takes a very firm position on these questions — to provide
comprehensive care without exception.

Within this framework, a continuous effort is made to educate
physicians, patients and the entire population to increase their responsibility for a healthful life and the prevention and early diagnosis of
disease. It is clear, however, that many of these efforts to educate and
train the population, particularly the young generation, have not been
successful. This is an area of research that needs international exchange
of information and methods.

Economics of Health Services, and the Biomedical Model

Of the many issues discussed at Noordwijk two warrant further
commentary in these editorial remarks.

44

Economics of Health Services

Concern about paying for health services — for the elderly, for organ transplantation, for illness related to harmful lifestyles—was a recurring theme throughout the conference. At times this concern was stated in the form of insistence that society, usually government, should find a way to pay for health services whatever the cost, as long as health and life-saving were at issue. At other times the concern appeared as a realization that cost escalation, as in care of the elderly, could not be indefinitely sustained, and that very difficult and at times tragic choices would have to be made.

The surprise was that this problem of inadequate resources to pay for desirable or even essential health services appeared as new to some participants. This is familiar ground in the Third World and it is probably true that it should be seen as a permanent state of affairs world-wide.

There is a clear need to recognize the inherent limits of resources, to become skilled at the application of criteria for setting priorities, to use these priorities to ensure meeting the most serious of human needs, and to promote social justice.

In the Third World, where extreme scarcity is the rule, the most important limit to consider is perhaps not a ceiling above which society should not pay, but a floor, a minimum decent level of care, below which no one should be pressed. The difficulties of implementing such principles are generally not technological but organizational and managerial. A number of Third World countries have prototypes of such systems — modest in content, affordable in cost, effective in dealing with some of the most pressing problems, and manageable.

> In the health sector we must become familiar with the economics of scarcity. And since scarcity is relative it becomes a common ground for all countries, rich and poor.
>
> J. H. Bryant

The Biomedical Model and Lifestyles

During the discussion on lifestyles, tension with the biomedical model became apparent. Dr Monique Bégin pointed out how the public is attuned to the biomedical model and is unlikely to forgo that model in favour of a lifestyles view of health and health care. The public belief in science and technology is equated with reason; talk of lifestyles is "softer stuff". At the health policy level there is little possibility of moving money from the biomedical model to healthy lifestyles. If the medical profession does not support a lifestyles programme there will be little progress in this area, and this support is not apparent.

We appreciate the clear and tough-minded analysis of Dr Bégin, and there is probably no reason to doubt the reluctance of the medical profession to take lifestyles more seriously, but there are reasons to pursue a more hopeful perspective. It is a paradox that it is biomedical science that has established the validity of the positive relationship between healthy lifestyles and increased life expectation. It is biomedical science that has demonstrated that many of the diseases of the developed world are preventable. As societies undergo transition from traditional ways of life towards affluence, a cluster of diseases increases in prevalence — hypertension, obesity, diabetes, cardiovascular disease, stroke, cancer. Some countries have reversed these trends. In the US, for example, death rates of cardiovascular disease and stroke have decreased by a third over the past two decades.

These are not fairy tales. It is biomedical science that assures us that these are demonstrable and repeatable facts. In some countries it is biomedical leadership that is addressing itself to these problems and calling for more serious attention to be given to healthy lifestyles, such as diet, exercise, and avoidance of smoking and other forms of substance abuse. It is possible that the lead in promoting this field will shift from epidemiologists and sociomedical scientists to biomedical scientists, and that the promotion of healthy lifestyles will be seen as more closely associated with the biomedical model and therefore more acceptable.

Perspective on the Conference

What can we say about the Noordwijk Conference on Health Policy, Ethics and Human Values? If we look at the purposes and strategies of the International Dialogue on Health Policy, Ethics and Human Values, it will become clear that the conference made exceedingly important contributions.

Consider, first, the goals of the International Dialogue:

To strengthen national capabilities for addressing and making decisions about ethical and human-values issues involved in health policies.

There is accumulating evidence that this series of conferences is generating increased capacities among the participants and their countries to function in this field. Additionally, recommendations will be forwarded to WHO for the development of mechanisms within and among countries for facilitating and encouraging dialogue between health policymakers and ethicists and concerned health professionals.

To contribute to improved understanding of the concepts inherent in WHO's goal of Health for All (HFA) particularly its values content.

Consideration of ethical questions suggested a number of interesting probes into the values associated with HFA — new questions emerging as to the meaning of *health*, new insights into the meaning of *all* (see discussion below).

To develop transcultural and transdisciplinary approaches and methods for working in this field.

The interdisciplinary and intercultural participation in the conference formed the desired mix. Did it work? One heard conversations suggesting that it did. After an extended debate one participant asked another: "Are you an ethicist or an orthopaedic surgeon?" The answer, "Neither, I am a minister of health."

To use improved understanding of the approaches of various societies to the ethical and human-values aspects of health policy, as a way to pursue deeper understanding of human values across cultural and political lines.

This was the third CIOMS/WHO conference in this series, involving different cultural, religious and political groupings, and others should follow. These conferences are built around issues — the meaning of human life, for example — that are the very substance on which cultural values and even political ideologies are built, and at the same time, paradoxically, are so universal in nature that they transcend the differences and become a basis for common understanding. Perhaps we can never know whether deeper understanding among peoples of the world actually contributes to peace, but one can know that peace is unlikely without it.

Consider also some of the guidelines to the International Dialogue:

The Dialogue should be more than a series of independent conferences — there should be an agenda of issues or themes, pursued and monitored over time.

The Noordwijk Conference was built on questions which came to the fore in Athens and New Delhi but it was enriched by planning in Europe and North America, and new issues raised at Noordwijk will be carried over to the next steps in the Dialogue.

Priority should be given to policymakers and policymaking.

Policymakers and ethicists have been involved together, a sensitization of each to the needs of the other is under way, and ahead is the possible involvement of WHO in promoting mechanisms for intra- and inter-country dialogue about these issues.

A research orientation is needed to facilitate comparison and transfer of ideas about interactions between ethical concerns and policy options.

After the Athens Conference Professor Robert Veatch prepared a tentative list of research issues. At Noordwijk some participants expressed interest in pursuing selected questions. The nature of the questions and the need to consider them locally in the light of local values and policymaking encourages a research approach.

Cultural issues and, particularly, value differences should be retained and protected in the Dialogue, or otherwise they might be overshadowed by technological questions and analytical methodologies.

Cultural values were not strongly represented at Noordwijk, possibly because so many of the participants were from similar cultural backgrounds. Participants from the Third World countries contributed to a broadening of the discussion, but the issues they raised were not the subject of workshop debate. Careful attention should be given to this matter in the future.

There should be sensitivity to the needs of the underprivileged and underrepresented sectors of the population.

Here again, interest in technology must be tempered by concern for equity and social justice. At the conference, the needs of the poor and the vulnerable were defended on many occasions — that ability to pay should not be a criterion in making services available; that being a victim of disease should not render one susceptible to invasion of privacy; that being elderly, especially one of the poor elderly, should not be a reason for losing the right to health care.

While there were many things the conference could have done that it did not, it accomplished many things that would have remained undone, and it enriched the agenda of the International Dialogue.

The Conference and Who's Goal of Health For All

For those who follow WHO's theme of Health for All (HFA), the conference raised interesting and important questions. To begin with, a simple listing of the major concerns associated with HFA indicates that the conference dealt with those themes more often as a natural part of the debate than as a directed effort to deal with HFA.

WHO's goal of Health for All calls for primary health care that will ensure:

Universal coverage according to need

Services that are effective, affordable, and culturally acceptable

Services that are promotive, preventive, curative and rehabilitative

Community participation so as to promote self-reliance and not dependency

Intersectoral collaboration

All of these concerns were discussed extensively during the conference, the first three in every working group, the latter two more sporadically, particularly when the debate focused on subjects with technological complexity.

More interesting were questions raised during the debates, which impinged on some of the ways in which human values serve as underpinnings for HFA:

Discussions on health care for the elderly raised questions about the meaning of *health*: Being free of disease? Having a capacity for normal activities? Being free of suffering? Being able to tolerate discomfort and lack of normal function? Having peace of mind?

How do length of life and quality of life relate to the meaning and value of human life and therefore to the definition of *health* in HFA?

Discussions on genetic screening raised questions about the meaning of *all*: as I consider decisions relating to my genetic self, is my responsibility to myself, to my family or to succeeding generations? The concept of *all* in a genetic sense requires an intergenerational perspective.

The concept of *all* was also scrutinized during the debate about the elderly. Should the elderly be identified as a definitive group within the population, because of their special needs, and because of the rising costs of caring for them? Or is there an ethical trap in the possibility of stereotyping the elderly and detracting from recognition of their heterogeneity and individuality?

49

Discussions of AIDS and other lifestyle problems drew attention to the risks of aggressive approaches to disease control, in which afflicted persons whose cooperation is needed most become isolated beyond the reach of helping and being helped. The importance of developing caring and trusting relationships between patients and communities was explored. Here, new problems were seen of extending services to *all*, including the alienated and the vulnerable.

Onward from Noordwijk — The Next Steps

Proposed follow-up steps emerged from the Noordwijk Conference:

I. *Reporting to CIOMS, WHO and the Government of the Netherlands*

The proceedings of this conference will be sent to those who have sponsored this work: to CIOMS member organizations whose continued interest and support is the engine that drives this effort; to WHO whose inherent concern for moral and ethical issues in the context of policymaking is central to the possibility of this effort having any substantial impact; and to the Government of the Netherlands whose openness to, and interest in, these issues draw our highest praise and gratitude.

2. *Establishing formal mechanisms for dialogue between policymakers and those concerned with ethical issues.*

Several participants, especially policymakers, reflected on the usefulness of the discussions and called for the establishment of permanent mechanisms within countries and among countries for sustained discussions between policymakers and ethicists and other concerned persons.

Attention was called to a possible prototype, the International Health Policy Research Program, sponsored by the Pew Foundation of the U.S., WHO and the World Bank, which seeks to establish mechanisms for policy dialogue between health policymakers and institutions and individuals who can do research on problems relevant to policy.

It was agreed that WHO should be asked to consider whether it might promote the establishment of mechanisms for sustained dialogue between policymakers and those knowledgeable about ethical issues both within and among countries. Meanwhile, the Netherlands Government has intimated its interest in reviewing the material developed at the Noordwijk Conference in the light of some of its current policy concerns.

3. *Deliberations at Noordwijk as New Resources for the International Dialogue*

The International Dialogue on Health Policy, Ethics and Human Values has been broadened and deepened by the Noordwijk Conference. The possibilities may surprise even the Noordwijk participants. It would seem that travelling the road from Athens to New Delhi to Noordwijk has resulted in the accumulation of a growing number of interesting concepts, challenging problems and interested people. The Steering Committee for the International Dialogue has promoted the notion of an international network of interested countries, institutions and persons, and it appears that this network is well along in its formulation.

Tentative plans are already under way for further conferences which will follow and extend the agenda of the Dialogue. Of particular importance is the possibility of carrying the four subjects of the Noordwijk Conference (along with others included in the agenda of the Dialogue) to forums for discussion in the Third World. But these discussions should be more than replays of Noordwijk, because these countries are at different levels of readiness as regards policy dialogue and applications of the technology, and the context of economic development and cultural values will be decidedly different.

Those who would carry the dialogue to these countries must be prepared to encourage a process, not simply to transfer technology and related ideas. They must be prepared to step down their technology, to engage in discussions that are earlier in their development than in their home countries, and to consider interpretations of ethical implications that are built on quite different cultural values.

As an example of the range of differences, compare a problem seen in screening procedures in Europe with a screening method in Pakistan. In Europe a major concern in prenatal screening is the frequency of false-positive tests for certain conditions in chorionic villus biopsy in the ninth week of pregnancy. In Pakistan one screening procedure involves measuring weight for age in small children to determine their nutritional status; here, the worry about false-positives or false-negatives arises from the fact that the tests are done by illiterate community health workers who must weigh the child and put a dot in the correct place on a chart. These women realize they must be able to count in order to place the dot correctly. One of them was heard to cry out: "I can't count! Teach me to count! I must not be left behind!" She could not count, yet she was trusted by the community and was the indispensable member of the health team for entering that community.

In this comparison, notice that while the technological sophistication differs greatly the ethical concerns are similar, and from the point of view of human need there is no doubting the weight of the problem in the Third World. Here, then, is a challenge to those in the North to extend their vast skill and experience with policy and ethical issues to constructive interaction with the South.

So the road stretches out ahead, beyond Athens, New Delhi and Noordwijk, to other places and other ideas. The content of the Dialogue in these settings will be determined by the concerns of those who are in policymaking roles and by those concerned with the implications for ethics and human values of the policy questions. Thus the patterns of exploration set in Athens, New Delhi and Noordwijk may serve the next rounds usefully, but the issues will necessarily have new determinants, and all stand to learn from the outcomes.

PAPERS AND DISCUSSION

Interactions of Health Policy, Ethics and Human Values — A North American Perspective

S. Gorovitz*

Over the last two decades, one major factor of change in health care has been a marked increase in individual initiative on the part of health care consumers — increased assertiveness on the part of patients and increased sharing of the responsibility that once was primarily the physician's. This increase in the autonomy of the patient arises out of a heightened respect for the dignity and individual rights of all persons, even when they are in the category of patient. To a great extent, patients and physicians have become collaborators in the management of patient care, and as a result medical care is in some ways more complex. The physician is subject to challenges of a new kind — an entirely wholesome kind, to be sure, but somewhat new. The authority of the physician has been reduced as the autonomy of the patient has risen to greater prominence.

The current scene is changing rapidly, however, because a major factor in the present reality of health care is the somewhat analogous emergence of a collective phenomenon of assertiveness about health care — but the new voice of independence and participation is that of neither the patient nor the health-care provider: it is some third voice. And these third voices — collective, institutional voices — are further diminishing the autonomy and authority of health-care providers and, to some extent, of patients as well. They are the collective voices of employers, insurers, the government, and even ideological pressure groups, each of which has some vested interest in the way health-care providers and patients interact.

So just when patients and physicians began to feel comfortable about working together in a context of shared information and shared responsibility, they noticed major assaults on their collaboration from these other directions. The result is that the transactions that take place within health care cannot be undersood solely as transactions between patient and physician or patient and hospital — at least one third party is typically also playing a major role.

With that observation as background, I shall now tell eight short stories about the various ways the ethical aspects of a question have influenced the setting of health policy. In each case, when I talk about the ethical aspects, I have in mind either the identification of values or the resolution of conflict in values. You have heard, in Dr Bryant's remarks,

---

* Dean, College of Arts and Sciences, Syracuse University, Syracuse, New York, U.S.A.

what some of these value factors are. I refer also to such factors, among others, as the relevance of a patient's age to that patient's entitlement to care, the value of health in competition with other values, the limits of reproductive autonomy, the scope of parents' rights with respect to the education of their children, and the conflict between public health considerations and questions of personal liberty.

1. The first story concerns an example of policy failure, but policy failure of a particular kind. The subject is sometimes referred to simplistically as "the problem of abortion," as if there were some single, identifiable problem of abortion; in fact, there is a large cluster of different problems. We have a policy on abortion in the United States of America which varies to some extent from state to state and certainly varies in its impact on individuals according to their economic status. It is not a stable policy: there is constant turmoil and complaint about it. The debate is bitter and divisive, and continues although since the Supreme Court's Roe v. Wade decision abortion has been available and legal, subject to certain constraints.

I characterize this as an example of policy failure in precisely the following sense. It is not a policy broadly accepted by the population. It is a policy actively opposed by significant constituents within the population. This failure of our abortion policy is an inevitable failure; there is no other policy possible which would not be comparably divisive. Any change in the policy governing access to abortion will, to the extent that it pleases some constituencies, and for that very reason, alienate other constituencies. There is no common ground of opinion about abortion that can serve as the foundation of a stable, uncontroversial policy. There will inevitably, for any policy, be some people whose views are not compatible with it. They will continue to press against the policy they find distasteful. I therefore believe that in a society as heterogeneous as that of the United States the problems of abortion are fundamentally and lastingly insoluble. I wish it were otherwise, but I believe that no entirely satisfactory public policy has been achieved because none is even in principle achievable.

2. The second example is quite different. I cite it also as an example of policy failure, but of a very different kind. It concerns *in vitro* fertilization as a clinical therapy and as a subject of research. About a decade ago, the United States Government imposed a moratorium on Federal funding, or conducting, of research involving human *in vitro* fertilization. A process was then specifically designed to clarify the ethical issues, and it played out in a clear and effective way. An Ethics Advisory Board, within what was then the Department of Health, Education and Welfare, conducted a broad inquiry into the ethical issues related to *in vitro* fertilization, considering the views of every constituency and holding hearings in every region in the country. The Board then issued recommendations sanctioning *in vitro* fertilization as a legitimate clinical remedy for certain problems and also recommending that the moratorium on Federal funding be lifted so that research could proceed in a limited and controlled way. For entirely political reasons, these

recommendations were not accepted by the agency which brought about the inquiry. They were not rejected either. They were, simply, received. Amidst the turmoil of our electoral processes and the currents of political debate, *in vitro* fertilization came to be viewed as a politically sensitive issue with respect to which it would be imprudent for political figures to sanction any change in policy.

We therefore have today the anomalous result that many years later the moratorium continues and no research is conducted or funded by the Federal Government into human *in vitro* fertilization. Nonetheless, as a clinical therapy it has become well and widely established in the private sector; there are approximately 125 private clinics in the United States offering *in vitro* fertilization. Their success rate is low, but improving. It is an expensive procedure and an uncertain one, and, to the best of my knowledge, the only widely available clinical procedure with respect to which the Government opposes the conducting or supporting of research into safety or effectiveness. This public policy failure, unlike the example of abortion, was not inevitable. It resulted from a combination of moral controversy in a medical context and political cowardice.

3. The third example provides a much happier story. A few years ago, a physician in the United States, noticing the plight both of those awaiting kidneys for transplantation and of certain impoverished constituencies in the Third World, established a business according to which he would function as a broker, enabling healthy but impoverished citizens of the Third World to sell one of their kidneys to Americans who needed one. This transaction, he argued, would be beneficial to all parties — what the economists would call "a Pareto-optimal exchange," provided only that certain safeguards were followed. The seller of the kidney could set his own price, and was to be well-informed and uncoerced. The broker would provide quality control for the medical aspects.

When the proposal first came to light, it was viewed by many people with resistance and by some with repugnance. Yet, it was not easy at first to explain just what was unacceptable about the plan, given that there was to be no coercion and the intention was to improve the life prospects of impoverished individuals while increasing the supply of kidneys.

The doctor described the situation as one in which there would be no losers. I accused him, in testifying before a Congressional hearing, of seeking to plunder the parts of peasants for profit. Under pressure, during the Congressional debate, he agreed he would consider impoverished Americans as sources of spare parts as well. In the end, the 1984 Organ Transplant Act included a provision making it a Federal offence to engage in a commercial market in transplantable organs.

What is particularly gratifying about this outcome is that the argument against the scheme was an argument entirely on ethical grounds — that is, given the realities of present social organization, it is true that some people are so poor and desperate and others so ill that for them such a transaction could make sense. However, our goal should not be simply to stand back and allow those transactions, but rather so to restructure the social context as to make such transactions no longer attractive. It is far better to respond to the desperation of extreme poverty and of life-threatening illness in other ways than by reliance solely on a free-market economy. The argument was offered that this plan was, after all, just the American way — a free market, operating without constraint. But this argument failed utterly. There was virtually no support at all for allowing this commercial market; in fact, the prohibition took effect before the broker had an opportunity even to start operating his new scheme.

This is a success story in respect to public policy, a story in which a medical issue with moral overtones was addressed on the merits, and a consensus emerged as a result of analysis and debate, leading to a stable and uncontroversial conclusion.

4. The fourth example concerns genetic therapy. By "genetic therapy," I mean such things as direct intervention into the genetic make-up of a patient in order to bring about modification of the patient's physiology in a therapeutic way — not germ-line modification but only somatic intervention. Probably the first disease to be addressed in this way will be adenosine deaminase deficiency, which is not widespread, but is likely to become technically amenable to genetic therapy.

In the early days of discussion about genetic therapy, many members of the public were gravely concerned that it might be used for socially devastating manipulations of human life. Long before the approval of any experiments on humans with genetic therapy, there had been an open, structured discussion and inquiry into just what gene therapy is, how it works, its perceived benefits, and its possible disadvantages. This process, through a publicly functioning committee of the National Institutes of Health, has so educated the interested constituencies among the public that this kind of targeted genetic therapy has become uncontroversial.

I cite this as another example of a success story. No genetic therapy has yet been done, but it is likely that in the foreseeable future it will be done. When it is done, it will not be viewed as ethically controversial, precisely because it has been anticipated, with a careful, open, and extended inquiry into the moral misgivings that some segments of society had expressed.

5. The fifth example is surrogate motherhood. Surrogate motherhood does not depend in any central way on modern technology, unless it involves the use of *in vitro* fertilization. It does not necessarily involve anything more sophisticated than artificial insemination; it may not even need to involve that. Surrogate motherhood has been a topic of discussion within the United States for many years. In the last several months, because of the Baby M case, it has received heightened prominence. In the Baby M case, a couple contracted with a woman to bear a child for them. The child was genetically fathered by the husband of the couple; biologically, the surrogate mother was the mother of the child. After the child was born, the birth mother — the biological mother — said that she would keep the child and break the contract. She was then sued by the contracting couple. The court hearing was long,

lurid, and nasty, and became a national focus of attention — a kind of real-life soap opera.

In the end, the court found in favour of the couple and against the biological mother, granting custody to the couple and upholding the validity of the surrogate mother's contract. This was a very controversial result. Many people thought that, in the interest of the child, the court could have granted custody to the contracting parents without upholding the validity of the contract.

We have 50 states, no one of which has any coherent policy with respect to surrogate motherhood. Legislation has been introduced in many states, in some cases to regulate surrogate motherhood contracts, in some to allow it but to forbid its commercial use, and in others to prohibit it altogether. We have here the opposite of what happened with respect to genetic therapy. We have a scramble of inquiry and debate coming after the fact — after the institution of surrogate motherhood, in an unregulated and uncontrolled way, which has already given rise to very visible and tragic cases, and perhaps others not so visible.

What is distressing about this policy situation is that for many years many people have been calling for systematic, sustained, coherent inquiry into what our social policy should be, but it has not occurred. The process may now be accelerated by the vivid reality of a particularly painful case. This is an instance of public policy failure, but perhaps it is correctable.

6. The sixth issue is a very general one, which I will introduce with an anecdote. When I was a visitor for a summer in Boston's Beth Israel Hospital in 1985, I kept hearing about a patient who was legendary in the hospital. Finally, I went to see her. Mrs T., 94 years old, was on life-support systems. She had been in the hospital for 14 months and was in the respiratory intensive care unit. This is not an example of a patient beyond cognition, whose life was being sustained to no obvious point. Indeed, for Mrs T. there was an obvious point. When I met her, she was watching a soap opera on television. She could not speak, but was staring at the set. I asked her if she watched this programme regularly and she nodded in the affirmative. I asked her if she would mind if I switched to a different one. She became so agitated that I thought she would separate herself from her various pipes and tubes. It was quite clear that, though her life was a very narrowly focused one, it had continuing value for her.

The cost of her care at that point had exceeded half a million dollars. There was nervousness within the hospital about the possibility that on any given day another Mrs T. might be admitted. The United States has an aging population, with 25 000 over 100 years of age. This number will rise rapidly in the years to come. We are able to sustain the lives of the very old and very ill unlimitedly, but at immense cost. The issue is now beginning to be raised in a most discomforting way: is it justifiable to place economic constraints on access to health care for the very old and very ill? This question in general has not been addressed because the discomfort of even raising it is so great. But, more and more, in hospital settings, the economic realities of our medical capacities in the context

57

of an aging population are quietly terrifying those who have financial responsibility for our health care institutions. Here is a public-policy issue where we have not yet even formulated the questions that will have to be addressed.

The last two stories concern especially pervasive issues, quite unlike those I have just told.

7. There loom over us all the darkening clouds of the AIDS epidemic. In every country the reality of AIDS raises many policy issues, and they are laden with moral content. They are not just questions of preventive strategy. In the United States today, one of the more interesting aspects of the cluster of debates about AIDS is the conflict within our own administration.

We have a Surgeon General — who, unfortunately, will not be with us this week precisely because of a major conference in Washington on AIDS — who has very forthrightly argued for an aggressive educational campaign as one important part of trying to control this epidemic. In particular, he has advocated sex education for young people. He works for a President who opposes this policy. It is a remarkable debate to occur publicly within a single administration. At the heart of this matter are many morally-laden issues. One is whether parents have the right themselves to determine what their children will be exposed to and what not, in their schools. Some parents believe that all matters of sexuality and morality must be left out of schooling. This view is a result of their belief that only the home or the church can adequately address these issues, and that, if the school does it, it will do it in some inappropriate way. Some people hold the view that to talk about sexual behaviour is implicitly to advocate it and that, therefore, if one believes, as the President apparently does, that the best way to avoid AIDS is abstinence, non-abstinence should not be discussed. In particular, therefore, one cannot make distinctions between prudent and stupid non-abstinence. This debate is raging right now, today.

8. I turn last to the leading preventable cause of illness and injury in the United States and probably in most of your countries as well — that is, smoking. The restriction of smoking generates controversy because it means that some people are less free to engage in behaviour in which they would like to engage, even if they are horrified by the fact that they do so. Many of the people who smoke find it appalling that they do so but are undeterred by this view of themselves.

In commercial aircraft the smoking section seems to get smaller year by year. However, no matter where I sit, I am aware of it when someone smokes, because it is a contained space and even one cigarette in the back row can affect someone anywhere in the aircraft. Many domestic flights in Canada do not allow smoking at all. We do not yet have that policy in the United States, but it may come. Here in Europe, where smoking is very much more prevalent than in the United States, I suspect you are far from that kind of totally restrictive policy.

Many United States companies have adopted restrictive policies, ranging from smoking only in designated spaces to no smoking during the work-day to a few instances in which company policy is "If you are a smoker you may not work for us no matter where or when you smoke." Such policies are motivated partly by employers' growing awareness of how much more expensive it is to have employees who are smokers. The restrictions also are prompted by the growing activism of non-smokers who wish to be protected from the consequences of other peoples' addictions.

In the public sector in New York State, we have a particularly intriguing situation, still unresolved. The Health Council, a regulatory agency, has promulgated very restrictive regulations. Every restaurant must limit smoking to no more than 30% of its space, if it has 50 or more seats. No smoking is allowed in any school building, from the lowest levels up through the universities. In various other categories, there are serious restrictions on smoking. But legal action has been brought against the Health Council by those who argue that public policy about smoking should be a legislative matter and thus is not a proper matter for a regulatory agency. They claim that the Health Council has the responsibility to enact regulations to do with sanitation and other such public health matters, but not lifestyle choice, not private matters such as whether people may smoke in a restaurant. So what we have now is a jurisdictional dispute about who has the authority to determine policy about the restriction of smoking. If the Health Council's position is upheld in the courts, where it is now under appeal, this can have national repercussions. If it is turned down by the courts, the matter will have been judged in the State of New York to be within the purview of legislative rather than regulative authority.

These eight examples refer primarily to processes of public policy and the influences on them of ethical factors. Clearly, ethical factors enter into the determination of public policy. Some people claim that policymakers are interested in the economic, medical, and perhaps the political aspects of health policymaking but not in its ethics. However, over and over again, in one way or another, ethical factors are either very influential or occasionally decisive factors in shaping a policy debate.

There is no common theme to these eight stories. Instead, there is typical American diversity: no single, coherent policy, no single process by which policy is addressed, no single forum in which questions are raised, no locus of decision where policy is resolved. Variation is wide from state to state, from issue to issue, from year to year. This is not a comforting observation, but from a North American perspective it is how it looks. I wish I had the knowledge to say more about other countries in North America than my own; what I have said has been thoroughly rooted in the United States. I offer you these reflections as a way of beginning to focus your attention on the ethical dimensions of determining public health policy.

Interactions of Health Policy, Ethics and Human Values — A European Perspective

Eeva Kuuskoski-Vikatmaa*

"Even the best of institutions is not capable of listening, empathy, embracing or loving. This can only be done by people."

These words are those of one of the participants in this conference, Dr Martti Lindqvist, in his book "Being human by profession". They crystallize the essence of health care: Man is at stake, we are to cherish his or her life and health, and not only treat cases or prevent diseases. This emphasizes also the ethical basis of health policy. The core of ethics consists of the personal values that guide man's actions and solutions. It does not mean fixed rules, official regulations, dictation or coercion. Ethics can only be based on free distribution and personal responsibility.

Health care is not an isolated section of society. It is an essential part of the culture, and within it the general values of society are reflected. The openness, pluralism and competing value-systems that exist in today's societies are increasingly reflected also in health care. On the one hand, the basic values of bioethics descend from the humanistic tradition which emphasizes the uniqueness, subjectivity, interaction, freedom and integrity of man and joint responsibility. On the other hand, the development of science and technology has brought forth the knowledge and skills and the many functions of modern medicine and health care. This development has emphasized efficiency and specialization, instrumentality, manipulativity and objectivity. Many ethical problems arise out of the tension between those different viewpoints.

Today's industrialized societies measure solutions increasingly by economic utility. This has inevitably had reflections in health policy, which again raises special ethical problems.

In everyday health policy the development of medicine and health care is decisively directed by existing resources, new technology and human values. In classical medicine there was a shortage of technical knowledge and skills and perhaps a lack of resources as well. Only few efficient methods of treatment and prevention were known, but ethical codes and traditions were numerous.

The development of technology has been exponential and it offers practical solutions to a vast variety of problems. Its end cannot be seen. The main shortage brought forth in public discussion seems to be that of economic resources. What is technically available cannot be universally applicable. There is a choice to be made as to who has access to treatment and when, etc. Compromises have to be accepted.

What are the criteria of selection? What is the decisive factor? Is it

---

* Member of Parliament, Helsinki, Finland.

money, a whim of chance, the patient's age or social acceptability, or are there clear views on the line of action in every situation? If so, whose views?

It may be that the main shortcoming today is, nevertheless, in the field of ethics. The ethical value system of man has not developed much since the ethical authorities of antiquity (Socrates, Plato, Aristotle, Jesus etc.).

Traditionally the ethics of research and medical care have been highly professional. Originally doctors developed their ethical codes. Later other health care professionals followed their example. Professional ethics will have positive value also in the future, especially in relation to internal relations within the professions, training etc.

However, it is evident that the mainstream of bioethics takes another direction. It increasingly implies wide interaction and cooperation of different kinds of people, groups, professions and organizations. Even the whole team involved in the treatment is as a whole an ethical subject.

Inherent in basic human rights is that all people may take part in decisions concerning themselves, their own lives and future generations. An "expert hegemony" is one of the dangers that the development of science and technology entails.

I believe that patients and patients' organizations play an important role in drawing ethical lines. At the same time society at large, with its institutions, organizations and the mass media, participates in formulating and applying ethical values. This extensive process might seem cumbersome, but there is no other alternative to democracy, cooperation and public responsibility.

Today in the field of biotechniques we have to take a stand on extremely complex and far-reaching problems. As examples can be mentioned genetic research, gene therapy and new reproduction technologies. How can we promote extensive ethical discussion concerning these matters? And how are we to agree on basic human values and assure the protection of these values in health care as well as in research?

The task of society is to guarantee that the citizens have sufficient information on, for instance, genetic diagnostics, gene therapy and the possibilities of treating infertility, the risks entailed and ethical considerations. This is important in order to allow people themselves, when necessary, to solve their own problems. But it is especially important because the lines for developing such measures must be publicly and widely and profoundly considered and debated.

The role of the mass media in ethical debate is crucial. When the media report rapidly and superficially on such ethically difficult and complex issues they decisively influence the development of the values of society. We should question whether the media fully realize their power of influence and their ethical responsibility in their news competition, and also when they treat of more common matters such as the care of the elderly, the situation of the disabled or the cases where attention is focused on a single narrow problem, separated from its wider context and background.

At the same time, the mass media form the necessary channel to cultural discussion on ethical matters. They reach rapidly and effectively a great number of people, often before the legislator has begun to tackle the problems.

In the welfare state, legislation is generally based on commonly shared ethical values. At the same time legislation may also change value systems. It might also, unnoticed, influence ethical values even before they have been under discussion and before the changes have been fully understood.

Today's political decision-makers have to enact laws which touch upon very difficult and sensitive areas of life from birth to death. For instance, it has become possible to keep alive patients with a "hopeless" prognosis. Consequently this has led to extensive discussions on whether the suffering of patients is sometimes unnecessarily prolonged.

The crucial question is: Do we have the right to do everything we can do? Who in our society are actually guiding and deciding what is to be done and what is not to be done?

Modern medicine seems to have reached a point where traditional ethics no longer suffices to control all of professional behaviour. Consequently demands are voiced on the need to formulate rules on research. Or have we already proceeded so far that the rapidly progressing scientific competition is left to find its own paths? Is the remaining task for the ethicist only to try to find acceptable justification for new inventions, to make everything acceptable and legal? Do we finally end up with quality control on human beings and eugenics?

The most important issue of everyday health care is, however, a continuous and confidential therapeutic relationship. This basis of healing and treating has, unfortunately, been pushed to the background in the euphoria caused by the advance of science and technology. We have created an illusion that technological equipment and new methods of treatment can replace this mutual and personal interaction between human beings.

My own experience both as a doctor and as a health politician is that the criticism of the Finnish health care system is growing from the underestimation of the interaction process in therapy. Patients have not been seen as individuals in need of help; they have been treated as "diseases and cases". The professionals have not shared the burden of their patients' disease or shown empathy amidst their haste, but have perhaps misused their power and acted as though they were superior to the patient.

There has been discussion on the "facelessness" of the health care system and on the "assembly-line" approach. Indeed there is something wrong in the system if it prevents the staff and the patients from creating durable therapeutic relationships and if it does not assure each and every patient of getting help as soon as possible.

In modern times Western culture has upheld the central ethical principle of the right of individuals to decide over their own lives provided that they bring no harm to their fellow-men or the essential functions of society. In the sphere of health care this has implied that the patient's informed consent is essential in all examinations, and in treatment and research.

In order that respect of informed consent and human autonomy functions, special emphasis should be given to the effort that the citizens may gain an integrated understanding of their own society, their risks and possibilities, and the function of the health care system.

If technological development and the increasing complexity of health care systems leave people at the mercy of expert opinion, the trend is wrong from the point of view both of individuals trying to cope with their own lives and of democracy.

Also, there are signs that the principle of personal freedom is being interpreted wrongly and with indifference. Researchers and health-care personnel do not always take the responsibility inherent in the therapeutic relationship but leave all choices and decisions to the patient. Psychosocial support of the choices made and confidence-building are lacking. This results in passiveness. Thus being a patient in health care is experienced as analogous to consuming. Health issues may be compared to the exchange of commodities or the supply of leisure-time service. Yet health is not a commodity to be bought from a shop.

Another noteworthy and undesirable development in the Western world has been increasing litigation against health care personnel in therapeutic relationships. Regarding the therapeutic relationship as mainly a legal issue of interests and controversy obscures the original purpose of care, whereas the fostering of a confidential relationship enhances the possibility of benefiting from technological advances in the interests of patients.

Man's illness and health are also reflected in social relations. Social phenomena produce their own pathology, but, with regard to recovery, social networks are also important. In the Western world help and substitution are sought within the health care system also for problems due to difficult or broken human relationships. In some areas, for instance in big cities, and within certain population groups, such as the elderly, the problem of alienation and loneliness is very serious.

The health care system cannot take responsibility for satisfying all the social needs of the population. The physician or the social worker can never replace a family member or a friend. Indeed, the health care system cannot even respond to all medical needs. Therefore we have to search for new methods and revive some old measures in order to enhance civic responsibility.

Basic care and human presence and warmth can be provided by any neighbour without a specialist training. Open care systems can be developed so that they provide the necessary and complementary support and assistance to the care given by the natural communities, for example in terminal care.

The extent to which it is possible to realize these ideas in daily life depends largely on the functioning of popular movements, basic communities and voluntary organizations within each society. These bodies express well the faith in life, cooperational capacities and the initiative of citizens. Lack of such initiative and voluntariness is a sign of serious disturbance in the relationship of the people with their environment and their future.

In the countries of developing free-market economies, with emphasis on competition, health care systems experience many of the harmful effects of competition. These circumstances easily lead to the appearance of so-called "B-class" or second-class citizens, who have no "useful" place in the productive functions of the society. Nobody needs them. As a result they easily become "labelled", and losing their self-esteem they become lonely and passive.

From the point of view of human values, the spread of competition within the health care system has to be strongly opposed. Bioethics cannot accept that human beings are classified as successful and unsuccessful, guilty and innocent. There can be nothing worse than morally labelling human beings on the ground of their disease.

It is also unacceptable to classify diseases into those acquired (such as pulmonary cancer caused by smoking, and cirrhosis of the liver caused by extensive use of alcohol) and other diseases. To the individual such a division is hardly ever relevant or justified. What is most important is to accept patients as they are, to share their problems at the personal level, and to mobilize such human resources as can enhance their faith in life and their capacity to cope positively with their lives.

For the Western industrialized world HIV infection and AIDS seems to be a crucial test of our ability to act rationally, humanely and responsibly. If we fail in this, we shall probably fail at many other levels and in many other ways as well.

Health-care systems and health policies have increasingly far-reaching implications for the future. This applies especially to resources, but also to improved diagnostic and treatment practices. If we create a mechanical and bureaucratic health care system, this will also produce mechanical and bureaucratic attitudes towards life as a whole.

People's faith in life depends largely on how secure they feel and how convinced they can be of obtaining human help in case of need. It is necessary therefore not to allow any "in-between" groups to develop within primary health care, and that health-policy experts and decision-makers have a clear view of the needs, circumstances and mood of citizens.

Pluralistic societies have in principle adopted positive attitudes towards different views, convictions and lifestyles. Also, health-care systems must adapt to such attitudes.

People's initiatives in self-care must be supported also when they reflect personal opinions and expectations. It is most important to eliminate economic and human exploitation and the risks to patients who resort to alternative treatment measures.

Diversity has always meant development potential biologically, culturally, socially and humanly. The challenge in Europe is greater than ever, since, more and more, Europe has become multicultural, from the contribution of migrant workers and refugees. This multicultural characteristic is likely to become more marked in the future. All groups are entitled to feel that they are being heard and accepted and they receive the help they need.

Today it is possible, and indeed necessary, to examine ethical questions not only as the ethics of care, but even more as the ethics of health policy and biotechnology. This is not to underestimate moral or ethical aspects at the individual level, but rather to view them within a wider frame of reference.

All the member states of the World Health Organization have adopted the goal of Health for All by the Year 2000. It is based on the principles of equity, solidarity and justice — a very clear system of values. Nevertheless, it has been argued that it reflects the norms and social attitudes of Northern and Western Europe in particular.

In Finland also we have drawn up our own programme for Health for All by the Year 2000. Two years ago Parliament discussed the Health Policy Report of the Government concerning long-term guidelines. It must be admitted that there was surprisingly little discussion on the ethical items of the programme, either in the preparation by experts, within the health administration, or in the political forum. Also prior to the parliamentary elections of March 1987 there was very little discussion on health care and its principles.

As far as health care professionals are concerned, the discussion has mostly been left to certain specialists and others with a special interest in ethics. The number of people taking part in the discussion needs to be expanded, and the field of themes broadened.

In the promotion of the health of the citizens, the traditional measures of health care are important, but also many other fields of societal life must be taken into consideration, such as lifestyles, nutrition, excessive use of alcohol and tobacco, traffic accidents and the health risks in the environment. These cause considerably more illness than such traditional infectious diseases as poliomyelitis, pulmonary tuberculosis and common paediatric diseases. Many of the health risks are related to economic questions such as unemployment, working-hour arrangements, price policies regarding tobacco, alcohol products and food, as well as advertising, environmental protection etc. What are the values which guide us in deciding these issues?

A more active dialogue between the health-care professionals, other experts concerned and policymakers is called for in order to create the basics for a safer and sounder human life.

I wish to thank the organizers of this conference most warmly and wholeheartedly. I am convinced that it is a significant contribution to broadening discussion and encouraging more people to participate in the ethical debate. I am sure we shall not find the final solutions to the questions, but even encouraging discussion is already a most valuable achievement.

Screening and Counselling — Ethical and Policy Aspects

M. A. M. de Wachter*

I. Genetic Screening

Genetic screening is the systematic research in a population for persons of certain genotypes. The usual purpose is to detect persons who, themselves or their offspring, are at risk for genetic disease or genetically determined susceptibilities to environmental agents.[1] The subject matter of this paper will be screening for genetic conditions, more specifically adult screening in the light of people's reproductive choices, and occupational screening for susceptibility to harmful agents and actual genetic damage. This field holds the promise of increasing people's options and letting them make informed and free choices.[2] The formal approach of this presentation is ethical: it considers screening and counselling from the viewpoint of right and wrong, of what ought and what ought not to be done if one is to act responsibly.

Screening is a medical procedure that may be chosen by an individual who desires information as an aid in making personal, medical and reproductive choices.[3] At the micro-level what is at stake is reproduction, occupation, and quality of life. At the macro-level what is at stake is public health and the overall quality of life as well as the values of our society. These two levels of concern are in themselves sometimes a cause of tension between the private and the common good.

II. Genetic Counselling

Genetic counselling is the provision of advice about the occurrence of genetic disorders and the risk of recurrence of a defective fetus. Clients or patients are informed of existing services, techniques, and alternative choices. M. W. Shaw has listed some of the objectives of genetic counselling, as follows:[4]

1. Directed at an affected individual

    (a) Decrease the pain and suffering of the disease.
    (b) Advise whether treatment is possible.
    (c) Quote risk figures for offspring and other relatives.
    (d) Reduce anxiety and guilt.
    (e) Help the patient cope with the affliction.

2. Directed at parents

    (a) Help couples make rational decisions about reproduction.
    (b) Give family-planning options to at-risk matings.
    (c) Reduce parental anxiety and guilt.

---

* Director, Netherlands Institute for Bioethics, Maastricht, Netherlands.

(d) Educate parents about the disease in question.
(e) Encourage couples to make their own decision.
(f) Discourage high-risk couples from reproducing.

3. Societal goals

(a) Eliminate genetic disease.
(b) Prevent genetic disease.
(c) Reduce the incidence of genetic disease.
(d) Reduce the burden of genetic disease.
(e) Decrease the frequency of deleterious genes.
(f) Upgrade awareness of genetics in the public.
(g) Influence mate selection.

This list is not exhaustive, nor does it express consensus among geneticists. Some geneticists will reject several of these aims, such as discouraging high-risk couples from reproducing. Some objectives, such as "eliminate genetic disease", are considered unrealistic, because recessive disorders will never be eliminated. Still other goals need refinement: some people think, for instance, that geneticists should not merely encourage but also assist couples to make their own decisions.

Nevertheless, the list clearly indicates that genetic services are not only directed towards individuals, parents, relatives and society. Consequently, public policymakers may become interested in the activities of genetic counsellors, such as:

- recording a family pedigree
- verifying the diagnosis of affected relatives
- determining the applicable genetic facts
- recognizing and dealing with the psychosocial implications of prenatal diagnosis
- discussing the potential problems of undergoing prenatal diagnosis with its various techniques
- discussing the decision a couple makes if the fetus is defective.[5]

In the Netherlands as elsewhere geneticists have developed a practice of ethics in view of the complexity and sensitivity of genetic problems. They aim "at providing all information necessary to enable the person being counselled to make his or her own reproductive decision in accordance with his or her own view of life".[6] Therefore, counsellors refrain from giving their own private opinions. Yet, in order to enable clients to decide for themselves, the counsellors are obliged to offer extensive medical and genetic information as well as prognoses. They must describe the various alternative solutions such as prenatal diagnosis, possibly though rarely followed by selective abortion, artificial insemination by donor (A.I.D.), anticonception, sterilization and adoption.

68

III. Policy Development on Screening and Counselling for Genetic Conditions

Both the USA and Europe have their ethical debates about screening and counselling. As far as policy development is concerned the United States of America seems to be in the lead. An example of policy development where ethical aspects are becoming an integral part was provided by the President's Commission for the Study of Ethical Problems in Medicine and Biomedical and Behavioral Research. In 1983 this Commission issued a report on the ethical, social, and legal implications of genetic screening, counselling, and education programmes. Its principal conclusions fall into five categories:[7]

(I) *Confidentiality*

— Genetic information should not be given to third parties without explicit and informed consent.
— Stored information should be coded.
— Confidentiality may be overriden to help relatives if simultaneously:
  • voluntary consent to disclosure has been refused,
  • withholding information from relatives will harm whereas disclosure would avert harm,
  • the harm to individuals would be serious, and
  • care is taken to disclose only needed information.

— Adoption laws should be changed to permit information about serious genetic risks to be given to the adopted or their biological families.

(II) *Autonomy*

— Compulsory screening is only justified to protect the defenceless (e.g. screening for phenylketonuria (PKU)).
— Individuals may wish to have genetic information as an aid in making personal, medical and reproductive choices.

(III) *Knowledge*

— Incidental findings (nonpaternity) or sensitive findings (XY-female) should presumably be disclosed.
— Genetics should be part of curricula from elementary to professional levels.
— Health workers should be trained in technical, social and ethical aspects of genetic screening.

(IV) *Well-being*

— Sperm donors for AID should be screened.
— Programmes should not be undertaken unless reliable results are assured.
— Programmes need a full range of prescreening and follow-up services.

(V) *Equity*

— Access to screening and counselling should take account of incidence in ethnic groups.
— Screening practices (e.g. for advanced maternal age) should be reviewed.
— Determination of high-risk group or of sufficient predictive value of a test requires ethical and technical analysis.
— Cost-benefit analysis does not provide a means of avoiding difficult ethical judgements.

It has been noted that the recommendations of the President's Commission are designed to protect primarily the individual from undesirable effects. Such effects will be minimal if screening programmes are intended first and foremost to maximize the options available to couples at risk of an affected child, rather than to reduce disease incidence.[8]

During research for this paper I explored the possibility of identifying specific European needs and policy requirements. The effort, however, seemed fruitless. The same problems occur on both continents. It may be true that in Europe counselling is more pragmatic and less defensive than in North America. Furthermore, solutions may differ from one European country to another and even within one country. The approach to beta thalassaemia screening in the two parts of Cyprus was found to be remarkably different. In the Turkish administration screening for carrier status was compulsory in order to obtain a marriage certificate. The Greek part rejected this as undemocratic and for some time the programme was blocked. Meanwhile the programme in the Turkish administration produced better results.

The difficulties in conveying adequate counselling to a whole community have in some cases been recognized at an early stage and acted upon.[9] The result in one case was a well-planned programme and a remarkable reduction of thalassaemia cases in the Cypriot community in London.[10]

IV. Ethical Aspects of Genetic Screening and Counselling

1. *DNA Analysis*

For years DNA analysis has been announced as the breakthrough of diagnostic power. The method is rapid, simple and effective. DNA probes were developed for alpha-l-antitrypsin deficiency, sickle-cell anaemia and a few other genetic diseases. It is likely that genetic diagnosis will allow for many more single gene disorders to be detected soon. The demand is for guidelines about the right use of DNA probes. How serious must a genetic condition be before we allow it to be diagnosed? Say we develop a sure test for presymptomatic testing of diseases with late onset, such as Huntington's chorea, how strongly could such a test be recommended to families in which the disease occurs? How much pressure is justified upon individual members of such groups? The moral issue is double. First, where does one draw a line of acceptable indications for prenatal diagnosis? Second, how free should individuals (couples) remain in determining their reproductive choices?

At present cystic fibrosis (incidence 1 per 2000 live births among whites) seems to be nearing the stage where within a given family not only can specific markers be used to trace the defect of the fetus, but also a direct genetic probe will be available. At what point of sensitivity and specificity does a test qualify for routine screening for cystic fibrosis of all pregnant women?

2. *Individual Rights and the Common Good*

A basic principle should be that generalized screening programmes must meet conditions of test accuracy, availability of counselling, and support services for those who are screened. A major source of conflict in screening and counselling programmes remains the tension between individual rights and societal interest. During the last decades Western medicine has aligned itself with the individualistic ethos of 'my life, my body' and all the rights this claim entails. If genetic medicine were consistent with the individualistic trend of the past, we would simply offer a free choice to parents at risk and let them choose freely among the available alternatives. Paradoxically, however, genetic medicine is turning the winds of individualism in more altruistic directions. Genetic information, for instance, is a striking example of a situation where rules of individual rights may have to be bent and reshaped. If such normative revolution occurs, it will be highly important that physicians, ethicists and politicians collaborate in shaping the new rules of genetics. Let us, therefore, take a closer look at the ethical issues of genetic information.

Information is power. This is true also of matters of genetic information about individuals, families, ethnic groups and whole populations. Genetic information primarily comes under the ethical principle of confidentiality, which protects information by bond, covenant or contract between doctor and patient. However, the very same information may be critical for others, e.g. relatives. By not giving information to relatives, for example in cases of autosomal dominant or X-linked diseases, the counsellor might impede personal decision-making by relatives. Many geneticists seem to believe that the rights of relatives to receive critical information override the individual's right to confidentiality. What are their arguments?

First of all, they say, this genetic information is of vital importance and may not be withheld from those whom it concerns. But what is vital importance? If withholding information would bring harm to others in their health, well-being and happiness, does the obligation to keep a secret then turn into an obligation to tell? If so, who should tell them — the doctor or the patient? Both lawyers and ethicists are exploring new ways which may lead to a structural exception to the rules of professional secrecy. In the Netherlands, for instance, a new bill on

71

the medical contract of therapy is proposing that people who are screened — whose data will be entered on clinical-genetic registers — be invited to consent to future use of the data in order that advice be given to relatives.[11]

A second argument supporting the communication of genetic information challenges the traditional notions of privacy and bodily integrity. In the past the limits of a person's body were considered to coincide with the territory of his own privileged knowledge. By giving the physician access to this most personal domain a person lost control of the use of this knowledge. Only with the person's consent was the doctor allowed to act on the information. Genetic medicine, however, is greatly expanding such views into a wider concept of corporate ownership of familial and ethnic autonomy. It now seems that the totality of a person's physical existence exceeds the limits of a single person's body. Some already say that genetic information is the common property of the family as a 'corporate personality'. Are we then entering a new era of medicine, viz. an era where information is governed not only by rules of individual confidentiality but also by the duties of common solidarity?

In developing new rules it will be necessary to fully weigh the dangers and pitfalls of structural breaches of confidentiality. Four such pitfalls are: (1) the mere biological link with relatives may be an insufficient basis for the intrusion into the psychosocial components of privacy; (2) it remains difficult to draw the line between medical information which is relevant to genetic counselling and information which is not relevant; (3) as ever more diseases will appear to contain hereditary components the breach of confidentiality is in principle unlimited; (4) perhaps a policy of taking away all data control from the screened will prove to be counterproductive and scare them away from participation in family programmes. What these points clearly prove is the immediate need to further elaborate the fundamental principle of "who owns genetic information", as well as practical rights of individuals and groups to process the information.

Since genetic information is highly sensitive and may trigger highly emotional reactions, it is not difficult to imagine situations where the owner would waive his or her right to know. Such may be the case in severe diseases of late onset such as Huntington's chorea or in diseases where no treatment is available. The trends amongst patients and their families, however, show a great desire to obtain information. A recent study attempting to assess the demand for presymptomatic testing found that, of 155 individuals at risk for Huntington's disease, only 15.5% refused the test as long as no treatment would be available, and only 1.9% still refused if treatment were available.[12] Traditionally the right not to know was acknowledged in medical ethics. Only when important decisions or weighty arrangements had to be made was the patient obliged to receive the information, e.g. about a terminal disease. The argument referred to the patient's self-interest in preparing for death and to the interests of others for whom the dying person had been responsible and was now supposed to make provision. In the case of families at risk

72

for Huntington's chorea it may be argued that the person is not about to die. On the contrary, he or she may be very healthy, showing no symptoms, feeling no signs of the disease, getting ready to marry and raise a family. For such a person a predictive test would offer several advantages (relief for non-carriers from fear and stigma, freedom to procreate without fear of abortion). Recently, however, the imminent introduction of an experimental programme for early detection of Huntington's disease has raised a few ethical questions. The first problem concerns the accuracy of the test and the possibility of inaccurate predictions. The second concerns the possibility that some of those identified as probable gene carriers will be unable to cope with the burden of this knowledge. Third, there is the possibility of misuse of information obtained from predictive testing.[13] These questions have been debated with the potential participants individually as well as with the National Society for Huntington's Disease in the Netherlands. It was agreed that great care is necessary in facing the novel issue of screening with 'delayed certainty'. Screening must be accompanied by counselling and support programmes before, during and after the test.

It seems that there is great pressure for more genetic information. Not only are professionals, public health authorities, employers and insurance companies eager to obtain such information, but also those who are screened have proven their ability to deal constructively with genetic information (despite some signs of ambiguity about when and how to obtain it). The Tay-Sachs programme in New York as well as the beta-thalassaemia screening in a number of Mediterranean countries have proven to be quite effective. However, mention must also be made of the controversial sickle-cell programmes in the USA. A major flaw in this programme was the widespread ignorance about the distinction between sickle-cell disease and the trait, that is between the disease and the carrier state, not only among the screened but also among employers, insurers and politicians.[14] *"Avant la lettre"* here was an example of how it should not be done.

V. Ethical Aspects of Cost-Effective Policies

Policy is all about organizing common activities of a given society in orderly, reasonable, rational and effective ways. Medicine is all about doing the appropriate thing in order to promote or maintain health as well as to prevent and cure disease. Ethics is mainly about analysing our intentions, our actions, and their consequences. Each discipline has its own approach to the many facets of life and consequently attaches different weight to the same events. The physician may ignore costs, the politician cannot. Cost-effectiveness is an iron standard of rational policy-making. Moreover, at a time of limited resources programmes and services must be allocated according to socially accepted standards.

Preventive screening for the fragile-X syndrome in Australia has been said to be cost effective. The cost of identifying one woman with the fragile-X syndrome was $3,570, a low figure compared with the estimated $1 million it costs the community to maintain a male with an intellectual handicap throughout his lifetime.[15]

In the province of Quebec, genetic screening focuses primarily on PKU, hypothyroidia, and tyrosinaemia. There is a special programme for Tay-Sachs screening among Ashkenazi Jews and one community of French Canadians. From 1969 to 1985, PKU screening was expected to save $31 795 589.15 in state expenses, $913 971.95 in cumulative national savings, and $227 723.30 in family savings. These estimates were made against treatment costs of $696 890.95 during the same period.[16]

Cost-benefit and cost-effectiveness in relation to both the economic aspects of, and the human values involved in, prenatal diagnosis are of major concern to decision-makers. Neither type of calculation is clear and easy, however, since it relies, implicitly or explicitly, on assumptions and evaluations that resist quantification. As one commentator has observed: "In general, one should be quite skeptical of such analyses and a full consideration of other than economic benefits in planning new programmes should always be carried out". Nevertheless, efforts at economic analysis have been made and are likely to be of some help.

The authors of one study calculated that for the prevention of Down's syndrome the potential monetary benefits would be greater than the costs in the case of women over the age of 40, about equal to the costs for those aged 35 to 39, and less than the costs if the service were extended to women under 35.[17]

From a study of cost-benefit ratios for spina bifida screening programmes, the same authors concluded that cost-effectiveness would apply only in a population with a high incidence of spina bifida.[18] Others, however, advocated early treatment of infants with spina bifida as most cost-effective.[19] Still others predicted that an alphafetoprotein (AFP)-screening programme for England and Wales would more than pay for itself within five years from savings in the cost of care of affected children.[20] In the United States, Layde and colleagues pursued the calculation of a similar AFP programme for spina bifida and emphatically stated that "the total cost of the programme to screen 100 000 such women was calculated to be $2 047 780 or slightly over $20 per woman screened, while the total economic benefits exceeded $4 000 000".[21] According to the authors, the favourable cost-benefit relationship gives the debate on ethics added meaning because the technical and economic feasibility of screening now puts the onus on its outcome.

Many analysts are aware of the difficulty in measuring such intangibles as parental distress, parental devotion, breakdown of the marital relationship, the quality of the life of affected children, and the loss of an unaffected fetus. The last possibility, for instance, would be unacceptable for some, no matter what its economic benefit to society, whereas others would see lost pregnancies as easily replaceable.

Cost-effectiveness remains a tool for decision-making. Quite understandably, policymakers also rely first and foremost, although not exclusively, on economic analysis.

Conclusion

Introductory notes which are meant to offer information for further debate should not end with conclusions. Questions for debate and issues to be solved would be more appropriate. To list all of them is not possible. It may suffice to mention but one, which may very well be the crucial ethical issue at stake. How can we integrate genetic medicine and technology into the way we live our lives? In other words, what are the conditions for a human and responsible use of the new field of genetics? To view genetics as a field that holds promise of a better life for many may lead to various interpretations according to one's social role.[22] The individual citizen, the geneticist, and the politician may approach the promise of genetics in very different ways. This conference is meant to tease out their opinions on the matter.

References

1   Rowley, P.T. Genetic Screening: Marvel or Menace? *Science* 225 (1984) 138.
2   President's Commission for the Study of Ethical Problems in Medicine and Biomedical and Behavioral Research, *Screening and Counselling for Genetic Conditions,* Washington, U.S. Government Printing Office, 1983, 104.
3   Id., 6.
4   Shaw, M.W. Review of Published Studies on Genetic Counseling. In: *Genetic Counseling,* ed. H. A. Lubs and F. de la Cruz, New York, Raven Press, 1977, 36.
5   Roy, D.J. & de Wachter, M.A.M. *The Life Technologies and Public Policy,* Montreal, Institute for Research on Public Policy, 1986, 69.
6   ter Haar, B.G.A., Genetic Counseling, in *Zorgen voor morgen,* ed. A. C. Drogendijk *et al.,* Nijkerk, Intro, 1979, 86.
7   President's Commission . . . , *o.c.,* 6–8.
8   Rowley, P.T., *o.c.,* 143.
9   Mouzouras, B.M. *et al.,* Thalassaemia as a Model of Recessive Genetic Disease in the Community. *Lancet* 13 (1980) 574–578.
10 Modell, B. Screening in the Cypriot Community in London. *British Medical Journal* 287 (1980) 1347–1349.
11 Gevers, J.K.M. Erfelijkheidsadvies en erfelijkheidsonderzoek. *Nederlands Tijdschrift voor Geneeskunde* 131 (1987) 456.
12 Markel, D.S. *et al.,* At-Risk Persons' Attitude Toward Presymtomatic and Prenatal Testing of Huntington Disease in Michigan. *American Journal of Medical Genetics* 26 (1987) 298.
13 Craufurd, D.I.O. & Harris, R. Ethics of Predictive Testing for Huntington's Chorea: The Need for More Information. *British Medical Journal* 293 (1986) 249–251.
14 President's Commission, *o.c.,* 21.
15 Turner, G. *et al.,* Preventive Screening for the Fragile X-Syndrome. *New England Journal of Medicine* 315 (1986) 609.
16 Dagenais, D.L., *et al., Evaluation de la rentabilité sociale du réseau génétique québecois,* Montréal, Ecole des Hautes Etudes Commerciales, 1980, 22–37.

[17] Hagard, S. & Carter, F.A. Preventing the Birth of Infants with Down's Syndrome: A Cost-Benefit Analysis. *British Medical Journal* 277 (1976) 753–75.

[18] Hagard, S. *et al.*, Screening for Spina Bifida Cystica. *British Journal of Preventive and Social Medicine* 30 (1976) 40–53.

[19] Shurtleff, D.B. & Lamers, J. Clinical Considerations in Myelodysplasia in the Role of Alphafetoprotein. In: *The Prenatal Detection of Open Neural Tube Defects,* ed. B. Grandall, New York, Academic Press, 1978.

[20] Glass, B. *et al., Towards the Prevention of Fetal Malformation,* ed. J. B. Scrincgeour, Edinburgh University Press, 1978, 217.

[21] Layde, P.M. *et al.,* Maternal Serum Alphafetoprotein Screening: A Cost-Benefit Analysis. *American Journal of Public Health,* 69 (1979) 566–573.

[22] Evers-Keiboom, G. *et al., Genetic Risk Perception and Decision-Making,* New York, Alan R. Liss, 1987.

Genetic Screening and Counselling — Implications of the DNA Technologies

M.F. Niermeijer*

Introduction

Five per cent of newborns have a physical or mental handicap, or both, caused by genetic factors.[1] In industrial countries, about one third of childhood diseases and deaths are related to this cause. A numerical or structural abnormality of the chromosomes is present in 1:200 newborns, leading to a combination of mental and physical handicaps (e.g., Down's syndrome) in most cases. Most are sporadic errors during distribution of chromosomes at the formation of sperms or eggs; a minority are caused by a chromosomal rearrangement in one of the parents with a high risk of recurrence in the offspring.

One per cent of newborns are affected by a single-gene defect, inherited as an autosomal dominant disease, with a 50% risk for a child of an affected parent (± 2000 disorders known), an autosomal recessive disease (± 1400 disorders known), with a sibling-recurrence risk of 25%, or an X-linked disorder (± 200 disorders known), giving a risk of 50% for the son of a carrier mother.[2]

A combination of multiple genetic and non-genetic factors interacting in a multifactorial process is the cause of malformation in one or more organs (such as congenital heart defects, neural tube defects, facial clefts, etc.) occurring in ± 2–3% of newborns.[3] For late-onset diseases in adults, such as diabetes, psychiatric diseases (schizophrenia, manic depressive psychosis), atherosclerosis, epilepsy, etc., a multifactorial causation is also implied.

About 10% of all adults, or close relatives, have a (partially) genetically determined handicap.

Exogeneous causes of handicap, especially at young ages, will be differentiated in all cases. They include maternal infections during pregnancy (rubella, cytomegaly, herpes, toxoplasmosis, syphilis, hepatitis, HIV-infection), maternal diseases during pregnancy (diabetes, thyroid disorders, certain genetic diseases such as phenylketonuria, myotonic dystrophy, etc.[4,5]), placental insufficiency, blood-group antagonism between mother and fetus, etc. Other harmful factors are maternal drug ingestion during pregnancy[6,7] (such as vitamin A and its derivatives,[8] anti-convulsants,[9] hormones, cytostatic agents, etc.), use of alcohol, nicotine, drugs of addiction,[10] and exposure to radiation or toxic environmental substances.[11]

* Professor, Department of Clinical Genetics, Erasmus University and University Hospital Dijkzigt, Rotterdam, Netherlands.

77

Approaches to prevention of genetic disease

1. General education on genetics and causes of birth defects

Teaching at secondary-school age on the principles of genetics, causes and methods of prevention of birth defects and genetic diseases may help people to perceive the need for genetic counselling in case of a previous affected child or the occurrence of a physical or mental handicap in a close relative. It may also be essential for the acceptance and utilization of screening programmes for carriers of specific genetic diseases in a population, like sickle-cell anaemia (in African and Mediterranean populations), thalassaemias (in Mediterranean and Asian populations), Tay Sachs disease (in Ashkenazi-Jewish populations) and — in the future — for cystic fibrosis (in Caucasian populations).[12-15]

Utilization of, for example, prenatal diagnosis of chromosomal disorders at advanced maternal age is influenced by availability of general information to the public.[16]

2. Screening for carriers of genetic diseases and chromosomal abnormalities in the population

The low incidence of carriers or balanced chromosomal rearrangements ($\pm 1:600$) and the high cost of chromosome studies at the population level make this approach impractical. Chromosomal studies in parents with repeated spontaneous abortions are useful for demonstrating a chromosomal rearrangement in about 4% of the cases in either parent, indicating the option of prenatal chromosome studies in a future pregnancy.[17]

Heterozygote screening, i.e. the detection of healthy carriers of an autosomal recessive disease, has become important for a number of diseases, especially if genetic counselling and prenatal diagnosis may be offered to couples in which both partners are identified as carriers with a 1:4 risk for affected offspring. Examples are: sickle-cell anaemia, the thalassaemias, Tay-Sachs disease, etc.[15] These programmes are especially important for populations with a high incidence of the various disorders.

A problem in this field is that these techniques (including subsequent prenatal diagnostic facilities) are not generally accessible to some populations with a high incidence of some haemoglobinopathies, as in Asia and Africa.

If the gene mutation or genetic defect in cystic fibrosis were to be determined[18] and a reliable method for population screening for heterozygotes became possible, this would lead to a large number of screening programmes among Caucasian populations.

3. Screening of newborns for detection of diseases, amenable to diagnosis and treatment

Many countries have programmes for the neonatal detection of diseases, usually with a low frequency, such as phenylketonuria, but with the

78

possibility of dietary or medical intervention, as in phenylketonuria, hypothyroidism, galactosaemia, maple-syrup urine disease, etc.[19] Depending upon local conditions neonatal screening may also be used for diagnosis and counselling, as for sickle-cell anaemia,[20] cystic fibrosis,[21] Duchenne muscular dystrophy,[19] etc., even when improvement of prognosis through early treatment may be still uncertain.[21]

4. Genetic counselling

Genetic counselling is the process of informing individuals and couples about their risks of having handicapped offspring, and about methods of reducing the risks. A diagnosis of the condition in a previous affected child, or of the handicap or disease in a relative, must be as precise as possible, since many genetic diseases show considerable heterogeneity.[2] Data from the family history and the medical-genetic literature are essential as well. To enable individual couples to choose freely between different options in case they are at high risk, many genetic counselling services will have a psychologist or a social worker to support them in making a decision that best suits their individual circumstances. The options available in the presence of increased risks involve refraining from reproduction, accepting the risk, insemination by donor-sperm or donor-ovum, utilization of prenatal diagnosis (if the disorder is detectable by chorionic villus biopsy in the 10th week of pregnancy, by amniocentesis in the 16th week, or by ultrasound fetal imaging), or adoption.

The implications of these options for individual couples and their moral attitudes and social circumstances highlight the need for a free and informed decision, based upon parental autonomy.[15] Genetic counselling services are a corner-stone in the prevention of genetic diseases, because most genetic diseases are not detectable by mass screening or other methods of carrier detection before becoming manifest in a patient. Most couples at high genetic risk will refrain from reproduction, or use one of the alternatives available.[22] This will eventually benefit both the couples and — in a more distant way — society.

In European countries the estimate of the need for clinical genetic services is one centre (with facilities for genetic diagnosis, chromosomal analysis, and prenatal diagnosis) for 1–2 million people.[23]

5. Prenatal diagnosis

Prenatal diagnosis of chromosomal disorders, neural tube defects (anencephaly, spina bifida) and some genetic metabolic diseases by amniocentesis in the 16th week of pregnancy was introduced in the early 'seventies and had a major impact on the reproductive options of couples at risk of these disorders in their offspring.[1] Ultrasound imaging of fetal structural defects made possible a clear visualization of brain, heart, kidney, skeletal and other malformations.[24] The acceptability of prenatal diagnosis was greatly improved in the 'eighties by the introduction of first-trimester chorionic villus biopsy, in the 10th week of pregnancy.[25] Transcervical aspiration of chorionic tissue became a safe method of diagnosing a chromosomal or metabolic disease, or a disorder detectable by DNA analysis, within a few days of the procedure. If an affected pregnancy is found, its termination is possible, upon parental request, by aspiration-curettage as an outpatient procedure.

Recent data indicate that chorionic villus sampling (CVS) is also possible in the second and third trimesters.[26] This together with improved techniques for ultrasound-guided fetal blood sampling (which replaces fetal blood sampling after intrauterine introduction of a fetoscope[27]) has resulted in much earlier and more rapid prenatal diagnosis. At the same time, not only do an increasing number of genetic diseases become detectable, but also more refined measurements of fetal health by fetal blood monitoring become possible.

The prenatal monitoring of large numbers of pregnant women because of advanced maternal age and the associated risk of a fetal chromosomal disorder has been called prenatal screening.[15] Similar testing in large groups is utilized for the risk of a neural tube defect, especially in high-risk areas, by combined maternal serum alfa-fetoprotein (AFP) measurement in the 16th week, and follow-up of increased AFP levels by repeat testing, ultrasound studies and amniocentesis. It allows the detection of around 90% of cases of anencephaly and 70% of the spina bifidas, with a low rate of false-positives.[28] Low serum AFP levels might indicate an elevated risk of a chromosomal disorder (like trisomy 21, Down's syndrome); about 25% of cases might be detectable in this way, after confirmation by amniocentesis in about 5% of the pregnancies.[29] Some centres are applying this option. This approach to prenatal monitoring, with a high risk of not detecting a serious chromosomal disorder, still needs a full assessment of its technical and ethical acceptability.[30]

Advances in genetic diagnostic technologies

In the field of chromosomal disorders, refined chromosomal banding methods have permitted visualization of smaller chromosomal rearrangements and deletions, and the delineation of a number of associated syndromes.[31]

A major advance was the detection of the fragile X-chromosome by using a specific culture medium. This chromosomal marker is the essential diagnostic sign of an X-linked mental retardation syndrome in males, responsible for about 11% of retardation among males. Female carriers, about one third showing mild to moderate retardation, have this chromosome in a varying number of their cells in about half the cases. Even with this still imprecise method for detecting carriers, the diagnosis of this disorder in a retarded male is extremely important for genetic counselling of female relatives and discussing options for prenatal monitoring. In the future, DNA markers on the X-chromosome may become helpful, at least in some families, for increasing the accuracy of carrier-detection and prenatal diagnosis.[32]

In genetic metabolic disease, comprehensive systems of metabolic studies in urine and other body fluids, supplemented by enzyme analysis for confirmation of the defect in a metabolic pathway, are increasingly used for early and prenatal diagnosis.[1,33,34] Refined methodologies such as mass-spectrometry and gas-chromatography allow identification of abnormal molecules. However, there are only about 200 established enzymatic defects, a rather small number when compared with the estimated number of 50 000 structural genes in humans.[2] The technical problems of detecting "new" enzymatic defects (of generally infrequent autosomal recessive diseases) are a limiting factor.

Syndrome identification, a corner-stone of clinical genetic diagnosis, has received increasing attention[2,3,35] and computer registries may become helpful in the future for the comparison of cases, with the rapidly increasing data from the literature.[36]

The DNA technologies to detect gene mutations directly in the genetic code, or to follow mutations by studying markers linked to a disease-gene, have opened up fascinating new approaches to diagnosis and prediction, and will be discussed in the next section.

DNA-techniques for the detection of genetic disease

With DNA-splicing enzymes, each recognizing individual and specific sequences of DNA-bases, small fragments of DNA may be obtained. After separation according to their size in an electrical field, fragments suitable for study may be recognized by probes. Radioactive or otherwise labelled probes are available now for fragments of all human chromosomes. They are prepared by DNA-recombinant techniques by multiplication of small chromosomal fragments in bacterial systems.[37,38,39]

Any DNA-containing tissue, such as white blood-cells, cultured skin fibroblasts, chorionic villi from early pregnancy, etc., can be used for prenatal diagnosis.

DNA-diagnosis has the advantage of being independent of gene function, and is even possible without knowledge of the gene-defect in the particular disease.

Sometimes, the precise identification of a mutation is possible, as in sickle-cell anaemia, alfa-antitrypsin deficiency, etc. In most cases, only the localization of a disease gene on one of the chromosomes is known. By the use of markers for polymorphic sites on one or both sides of the gene of interest, a diagnosis may be possible (Fig. 1). Polymorphic sites showing inheritable changes in the composition of DNA-bases are ubiquitous in the chromosomes. These polymorphisms are detectable by DNA-splicing (restriction) enzymes and may be exploited as a marker for the disease gene of interest. The informative value of a certain polymorphic marker has to be established in every single family under

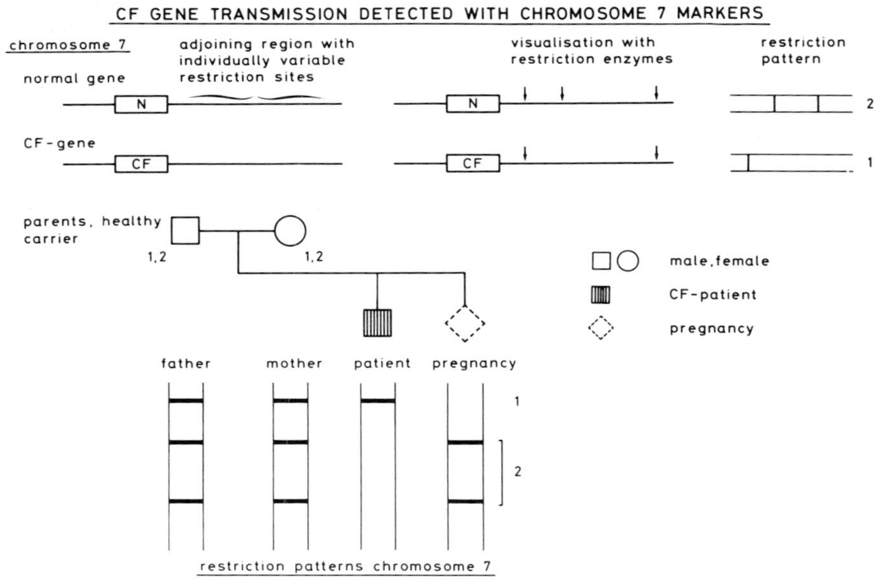

Fig. 1. *DNA-marker study for an autosomal-recessive disease (cystic fibrosis (CF)) prior to prenatal diagnosis. The pattern of markers is established in the affected child and the parents. Every single family will have its individual pattern.*

study. This information is also influenced by the frequency of the marker in the population under study, and the distance between the marker and the disease gene. If there is a relatively long distance, recombination may occur during formation of sperms or eggs. The risk of imprecise prediction may be reduced by using markers on both sides of the disease gene. Since markers are available covering the majority of the number of human chromosomes, localization of disease-related genes and establishing clinically informative polymorphic marker systems are only a matter of time.

Application of DNA-marker studies

1. Carrier-detection of genetic disease

Imprecise classical methods for detecting carriers of X-linked disorders (as limited by inactivation of one X-chromosome in a carrier female), as for Duchenne muscular dystrophy and haemophilia, are being rapidly replaced by DNA-methods. These are independent of gene-expression and allow the precise identification of both carrier and non-carrier states. Prenatal diagnosis by CVS and DNA analysis allow a carrier to have healthy sons.[40,41] This is a great improvement on previous prenatal diagnosis, when termination of all male pregnancies was one of the few

82

options available. With the high number of markers available on the X-chromosome, genetic counselling for X-linked diseases will develop a high degree of precision.

Carrier detection of autosomal recessive disease by DNA techniques at the population level is limited at present to a very few diseases where a gene probe directly detecting the mutation itself is available, as for alfa-antitrypsin deficiency and sickle-cell anaemia; conventional techniques for these diseases are, however, generally available. Since for most autosomal recessive diseases the markers are linked to the disease gene, carrier detection is only possible in families after having an affected child (Fig. 1. Table 1). Determination of the gene defect for cystic fibrosis[18] would induce a large number of screening programmes among Caucasian populations, which have a heterozygote frequency of 1:30 to 1:25.

In autosomal dominant inherited disorders, the heterozygote (carrying one normal and one abnormal gene) has symptoms of the disease, with a 50% risk of transmission to the offspring. The chromosomal localization

Table 1. Some diseases detectable by DNA-analysis

Disease	Frequency	Inheritance	Chromosome localisation
Thalassaemia (Mediterranean/Asian populations)	1 à 2:100	ASR	11,16
Sickle-cell anaemia (African populations)	1 à 2:100	ASR	11
Anti-trypsin deficiency	1:1500	ASR	14
Cystic fibrosis	1:3600	ASR	7
Phenylketonuria	1:10.000	ASR	12
Adrenogenital syndrome (21-hydroxylase deficiency)	1:10.000	ASR	6
Duchenne muscular dystrophy	1:6000	XLR	X
Haemophilia A/B	1:10.000	XLR	X
Hypercholesterolaemia Type II A	1:500	ASD	19
Polycystic kidneys (adult type)	1:2500	ASD	16
Neurofibromatosis	1:3000	ASD	17
Huntington's chorea	1:10.000	ASD	4
Myotonic dystrophy	1:5000	ASD	19
Polyposis coli	1:10.000	ASD	5
Tuberous sclerosis	1:30.000	ASD	9

ASR/D = Autosomal Recessive/Dominant
XLR = X-linked recessive.
Prenatal diagnosis in some diseases still limited by high recombination risk.

of a number of frequent disorders and the availability of DNA markers allow the transmission of the disease-related gene to be followed within families. The options in genetic counselling, and the specific problems in presymptomatic diagnosis of late-onset diseases, are discussed in the following sections.

2. Prenatal diagnosis

Disorders detectable by DNA-linkage methods can be easily diagnosed by first-trimester fetal diagnosis, by means of CVS in the 10th week of pregnancy, and a result is available in about two weeks. Significant improvements have become possible therefore. This is especially clear in the haemoglobinopathies, where analysis of fetal blood obtained by fetoscopy or ultrasound-guided umbilical-cord puncture in the 18th–20th week of pregnancy could largely be replaced by CVS and DNA-analysis.[42] Making these techniques available to the populations most in need of these advances remains an important task.

Cystic fibrosis is another example of a serious genetic disease that can be detected prenatally in pregnancies of parents who have previously had an affected child, by means of markers on chromosome 7.[43] This technique replaces the less sensitive and more indirect test of intestinal (microvillar) enzymes in the amniotic fluid.[44] The latter test is still important for parents after the death of an affected child, if no cells for DNA analysis have been stored.

A number of autosomal-dominant diseases, some with symptoms occurring during or after the second and third decade, are detectable by prenatal diagnosis; examples are Huntington's chorea, polycystic kidney disease, tuberous sclerosis, and conditions associated with cancer, such as polyposis coli. For Huntington's disease, an exclusion test (by checking for the affected grandparental chromosomes in a fetus at risk) has been proposed, allowing pregnancy termination in case of a 50% risk of the disorder, without informing the parent of his or her genetic risk.[45]

3. Presymptomatic diagnosis for late-onset genetic disease

With the increasing number of genetic diseases localized (and detectable by suitable markers) on the human chromosomes, many disorders, clinically detectable only in later life, may be precisely identified by gene-linkage studies. The most discussed example is Huntington's chorea[46-49] but in other disorders similar problems will be encountered.

Huntington's chorea or disease, with an incidence of 1:10000 in Caucasian populations, shows an onset of progressive neurological (chorea, athetosis) and mental (dementia) dysfunction before the age of 40 years in about half of patients, and later in life in the others. There is no medical treatment; only supportive care is possible during the duration of the disease (10–15 years). Risk-carriers (50% when a parent is affected, 25% if a grandparent is affected) may wish to be certain about their fate rather than to live in prolonged uncertainty. They can then make responsible decisions about their own and their families' future.

DNA-linkage studies allow prediction at present with a 95% level of accuracy, and an even higher level is forseen. The acceptance of such a test among risk-carriers has been shown to range from 60 to 80%; however, between 20 and 30% changed their mind just before the test,[48] showing the psychological problems of exchanging uncertainty (and the hope of a positive outcome) for certainty about one's fate.

The psychological burden of this type of knowledge has to be fully evaluated during introduction of these programmes in centres that provide adequate psychological support and extensive counselling as essential elements,[49] including also preventing the risk of suicide. Among the guidelines defined are a full, informed decision process, without interference by third parties (autonomy), no testing of minors or relatives who do not wish to know, no information to employers and insurance companies, etc. Participation of relatives (both affected and unaffected) is essential to establish the relation between the genetic marker and the disease gene in the particular family. The decision to participate in this type of study may be even more difficult if the disease in question is of late onset, like Alzheimer's[50] disease, where decades of productive life may antecede the onset of disease. These factors will also influence decisions to use prenatal diagnosis for this type of disorder.

Presymptomatic diagnosis may become very important for purely medical and genetic counselling purposes, as in autosomal dominant disorders with a very high degree of clinical variability in symptoms, like neurofibromatosis,[51] tuberous sclerosis,[52] and others.

In genetic diseases associated with cancer, such as polyposis coli (an autosomal dominant form of multiple colonic polyps and colonic carcinoma), DNA marker studies[53] may become helpful for differentiating between gene carriers and non-carriers. Carriers may be given the preventive option of early colectomy and genetic counselling and non-carriers can be spared periodic and costly colonoscopic follow-up studies.

DNA-markers will certainly be detected for a number of so-called common diseases, with a frequency of $+1\%$ in populations, and usually caused by a multifactorial mechanism in which multiple genetic factors interact in an additive way with largely unknown exogenous factors. Examples are atherosclerosis, epilepsy, manic depressive psychosis and schizophrenia, and diabetes mellitus. One may expect that no single marker or disease gene will be involved, as has already been shown for manic depressive psychosis, segregating with a chromosome 11 marker in one population (the Old Order Amish)[54] but not in others; X-linkage was found in other families.[55] Genetic heterogeneity (different genes causing the same clinical disease) may be one explanation; the other may be the presence of multiple genetic factors rather than a single factor in a multi-causal disease.

Still, there may be increasing pressure, with different goals, to use such imperfect markers by public health authorities — for prevention, risk-group determination, and intervention — and by insurance companies and even employers.

Gene therapy and manipulation of germ-line DNA

Gene therapy, by inserting a normal gene into the cells of an affected individual, may be possible for a very few autosomal recessive diseases. In autosomal dominant diseases it would be necessary to remove or repair the abnormal gene, which is not feasible at present. For a limited number of, generally rare, genetic diseases evidence of correction of a gene defect has been obtained by introducing a "normal" gene into cells grown in the laboratory.[56,57] Sufficient evidence must be obtained about the safety of these procedures — for example, about the risk of transforming the cells into malignant cells or introducing new mutations; of introducing the new gene into the germ line; of passage of the gene to other persons, etc. In their use of strict protocols and their need to be accepted by medical ethical committees, these procedures seem in principle not different from other new forms of medical therapy.

Since bone-marrow cells are the easiest and safest to obtain in humans, this approach will be largely limited to disorders manifesting in bone-marrow cells, e.g., sickle-cell anaemia, thalassaemia and some immuno-deficiency diseases such as adenosinedeaminase or nucleoside phospho-rylase deficiency. In other disorders the corrective effect may be mediated by enzymes or proteins produced by bone-marrow cells, as in antitrypsin-deficiency, haemophilia, and possibly some metabolic diseases. For metabolic defects principally manifesting in the brain or the liver, there are more difficult barriers to be overcome.

It is foreseeable that a limited number of clinical experiments under strictly controlled conditions will be performed in the near future, but that the impact of gene therapy will be limited in the coming years.

Manipulation of genes in germ cells[56,57] is another technique which is more widely discussed than its potential in practice warrants. Adding "normal" genes to a sperm, egg or embryo would need the prior removal of the defective gene, and the certainty that the "new" gene is integrated not only in a dose-controlled way (only one copy) but also at the exact correct position on the chromosome. Moreover, reliable techniques would be needed to test the final result, either in the germ-cell or in the embryo (for instance, at the 8-cell stage, etc.). For these and other reasons, no expert in the field would try such experiments in humans. Accordingly there is no reason for the fear that germ-line genetic manipulation would be used to create or help to select for certain desirable genotypes, whatever the type of "desirable" trait might be.

Social consequences of genetic disease and the "new" genetics

Genetic disease may be viewed as a disorder for which a variant DNA sequence is a major determinant and which manifests itself in impairment, disability and handicap, with some disadaptative consequences for the individual.[58] This concept brings genetic disease within the WHO concept of disease.[59] Besides the easily recognized life-time problems and limitations for affected individuals and their families, a greater number of associated social problems are to be expected now that the diagnostic methodologies, especially for late-onset diseases, are increasing dramatically.

In genetic counselling on reproductive options for parents in the case of an increased risk, freedom of choice is the predominant principle in Western societies. Still, there is a risk of social pressure to make decisions which are profitable for society, such as to use prenatal diagnosis in certain cases. This is partly based upon the unjustified expectation that nearly all genetic handicaps or diseases are detectable by prenatal diagnosis or predictable in genetic counselling. Most geneticists feel that such pressure is unwarranted. Since most genetic diseases and birth defects are caused by sporadic events (gene mutations, chromosomal errors during formation of gametes, unpredictable combinations of parental genes, and exogenous factors), there is no reason for placing a specific burden on couples who happen to have their risks determined.

Use of genetic tests might become required — or be proposed — for applications for jobs or insurance cover. This would extend the already existing problem that many prognostic risk data are available through a simple family history, whereas many countries have laws enabling both future employers and insurance companies, especially for life and disability insurance, to ask certain questions, and obliging the applicant for employment or insurance cover to answer. Individuals carrying a certain genetic risk might perceive a conflict of beneficence towards themselves or their families and towards their employers and co-workers.[47] Exclusion from work, for example, because of risk of a genetic disease, is warranted only if the onset of the disease would induce a severe risk to the company or to other workers, and if a high-accuracy test were available, and if only a limited number of people would be excluded.[47]

These developments need discussion in individual societies between politicians, government, employers, employees and patient organizations, with support from geneticists, ethicists and lawyers.[60] Otherwise, many more people might become socially handicapped because of inability to obtain employment or insurance necessary for social functioning, only because of a certain genetic predisposition. Those who would be identified, and only by chance, would be carrying the "burden" of genetic disease, whereas everybody carries some five to ten deleterious genes. It is necessary to share the responsibility of the human genome in a more balanced way. This will also preserve the acceptability of genetic diagnostic and predictive facilities, which have created new options for individual choices in life and in reproduction, beneficial for many individuals and couples at risk.

References

1 Galjaard, H. *Genetic metabolic diseases: early diagnosis and prenatal analysis.* Elsevier/North Holland. Amsterdam, 1980.
2 McKusick, V.A. *Mendelian Inheritance in Man,* 7th ed. The Johns Hopkins University Press, Baltimore, 1986.
3 Smith, D.W. *Recognizable patterns of human malformation,* 3rd ed., Saunders Company, Philadelphia, 1982.
4 Schulman, J.D. Simpson, J.L. *Genetic diseases in pregnancy. Maternal effects and fetal outcome.* Academic Press, New York 1981.
5 Goldstein, P.J. (ed) *Neurological disorders of pregnancy.* Futura Publ Comp. Mount Kisco, 1986.
6 Briggs, G.G., Freeman, R.K., Yaffe, S.J. *Drugs in pregnancy and lactation,* 2nd ed. Williams & Wilkins, Baltimore, 1986.
7 Schardein, J.L. *Chemically induced birth defects.* Marcel Dekker, New York, 1985.
8 Lammer, E.J. et al, Retinoic acid embryopathy. *New Engl J Med* 1985; 313: 837–41.
9 Lindhout, D. & Meinardi, H. Spina bifida and in-utero exposure to valproate. *Lancet* 1984; 2: 396.
10 Bingol, N. et al, Teratogenicity of cocaine in humans. *J Pediat* 1987; 110: 93–6.
11 Barlow, S.M., Sullivan, F.M. *Reproductive hazards of industrial chemicals.* Acad Press, London, 1982.
12 Scriver, C.R. et al. Beta-thalassemia disease prevention: genetic medicine applied. *Am J Hum Genet* 1984; 36: 1024–38.
13 Modell, B., Mouzouras, M. Social consequences of introducing antenatal diagnosis for thalassemia. *Birth Def: Orig Art Ser* 1982; 18: 285–91.
14 Clow, C.L., Scriver, C.R. Knowledge about and attitudes towards genetic screening among high-school students: the Tay-Sachs experience. *Pediatrics* 1977; 59: 86–91.
15 Rowley, P.T. Genetic screening: marvel or menace. *Science* 1984: 225: 138–44.
16 Mikkelsen, M. et al. The impact of legal termination of pregnancy and of prenatal diagnosis on the birth prevalence of Down Syndrome in Denmark. *Am J Hum Genet* 1983; 47: 123–31.
17 Sachs, E.S. et al. Chromosome studies of 500 couples with two or more abortions. *Obstet Gynec* 1985; 65: 375–8.
18 Estivill, X. et al. A candidate for the cystic fibrosis locus isolated by selection for methylation-free islands. *Nature* 1987; 326: 840–5.
19 Bickel, H. et al. Neonatal Mass screening for metabolic disorders. *Eur J Pediat* 1981; 137: 133–9.
20 Wethers, D.L., Grover, R. Screening the newborn for Sickle cell disease: is it worth the effort? In: Carter, T.P., Willey, A.M. (eds): *Genetic disease: screening and management.* Liss, New York, 123–36, 1986.
21 Dauphinais, R.M. et al Cystic fibrosis: early detection and clinical course. In: Carter, T.P., Willey, A.M. (eds): *Genetic disease: screening and management.* Liss, New York, 65–80, 1986.

22   Emery, A.E.H. Changing patterns in a genetic counselling clinic. In: Lubs, H.A., de la Cruz, F. (eds) *Genetic counselling.* Raven, New York, 113–20, 1977.
23   Passarge, E., Vogel, F. The delivery of genetic counselling services in Europe. Hum Genet 1980; 56: 1–5.
24   Hansmann, M. et al. *Ultraschalldiagnostik in Geburtshilfe und Gynäkologie.* Springer, Berlin, 1985.
25   Fraccaro, M., Simoni, G., Brambati, B. (eds) *First trimester fetal diagnosis.* Springer, Berlin 1985.
26   Nicolaides, K.H. et al. Why confine chorionic villus (placental) biopsy to the first trimester? *Lancet* 1986; 1: 543–4.
27   Daffos, F. et al. Fetal blood sampling during pregnancy with use of a needle guided by ultrasound: a study of 606 consecutive cases. *Am J Obstet Gynecol* 1985; 153: 655–60.
28   Wald, N.J., Cuckle, H.S. Open neural tube defects. In: Wald, N.J. (ed) *Antenatal and neonatal screening.* Oxford Univ Press, Oxford. 25–73, 1984.
29   Schoenfeld DiMaio, M. et al. Screening for fetal Down's syndrome in pregnancy by measuring maternal serum alpha-fetoprotein levels. *New Engl J Med* 1987; 317: 342–6.
30   American Society of Human Genetics: Policy statement for maternal serum alfa-fetoprotein screening programs and quality control for laboratories performing maternal serum and amniotic fluid assays. *Am J Hum Genet* 1987; 40: 75–82.
31   Yunis, J.J., Lewandowski, R.C. High resolution cytogenetics. *Birth Def: Orig Art Ser* 1983; 19(5): 11–37.
32   Opitz, J.M., Reynolds, J.F., Spano, L.M. (editors). *X-linked mental retardation* 2. Alan Liss Inc. New York. 1986.
33   Jellum, E. et al. Systemic laboratory diagnosis of human metabolic disorders. *Scand J Clin Lab Invest* 1986; 46: suppl 184; 11–20.
34   Stanbury, J.B. et al (eds). *The metabolic basis of inherited disease.* 5th edit. McGraw-Hill, New York, 1983.
35   Wiedemann, H.R. et al. *Characteristic syndromes.* Wolfe Med Publ. London, 1985.
36   Winter, R.M. et al. A computerised data base for the diagnosis of rare dysmorphic syndromes. *J Med Genet* 1984; 21: 121–3.
37   Weatherall, D.J. *The new genetics and clinical practice.* Oxford Univ Press, Oxford, 1985.
38   Steel, C.M. The tools, part I. *Lancet* 1984; 2: 908–11.
39   Weatherall, D.J. Implications for medical practice and human biology. *Lancet* 1984; 2: 1440–4.
40   Bakker, E. et al. DNA probe analysis for carrier detection and prenatal diagnosis of Duchenne muscular dystrophy: a standard diagnostic procedure. *J Med Genet* 1986; 23: 573–80.
41   Bröcker-Vriends, A.H.J.T. et al. *Genotype assignment of haemophilia A by use of a intragenic and extragenic restriction fragment length polymorphisms.* Thromb & Haemost 1987; 57: 131–6.
42   Kan, Y.W., The William Allen memorial award address: Thalassemia: molecular mechanism and detection. *Am J Hum Genet* 1986; 38: 4–12.
43   Williamson, R. The cystic fibrosis locus: a progress report *Disease Markers* 1987; 5: 59–63.
44   Kleijer, W.J. et al. Amniotic fluid disaccharidases in the prenatal detection of cystic fibrosis. *Prenat Diagn* 1985; 5: 135–43.

45   Quarrell O.W.J. et al. Exclusion testing for Huntington's disease in pregnancy with a closely linked DNA-marker. *Lancet* 1987; 1: 1281–3.

46   Shaw, M.W. Testing for the Huntington gene: a right to know, a right not to know, or a duty to know. *Amer J Med Genet* 1987; 26: 243–6.

47   Lamport, A.T. Presymptomatic testing for Huntington chorea: ethical and legal issues. *Amer J Med Genet* 1987; 26: 307–14.

48   Mastromauro, C. et al. Attitudes towards presymptomatic testing in Huntington disease. *Am J Med Genet* 1987; 26: 271–82.

49   Craufurd, D.I.O., Harris, R. Ethics of predictive testing for Huntington's chorea: the need for more information. *Brit Med J* 1986; 293: 249–51.

50   St. George-Hyslop. et al. The genetic defect causing familial Alzheimer's disease maps on chromosome 21. *Science* 1987; 235: 885–90.

51   Barker, D. et al. Gene for von Recklinghausen Neurofibromatosis is in the pericentromeric region of chromosome 17. *Science* 1987; 236: 1100–3.

52   Connor, J.M. et al. First trimester prenatal exclusion of tuberous sclerosis. *Lancet* 1987; 1: 1269.

53   Bodmer, W.F. et al. Localization of the gene for familial adenomatous polyposis on chromosome 5. *Nature*, 1987; 328: 614–6.

54   Egeland, J.A. et al. Bipolar affective disorders linked to DNA markers on chromosome 11. *Nature* 1987; 325: 783–87.

55   Mendelwicz, J. et al. Polymorphic DNA marker on X chromosome and manic depression. *Lancet* 1987; 1: 1230–3.

56   Ledley, F.D. Somatic gene therapy for human disease: background and prospects. Part I. *J Pediat* 1987; 110: 1–8.

57   Ledley, F.D. Somatic gene therapy for human disease: background and prospects. Part II. *J Pediat* 1987; 110: 167–74.

58   Costa, T. et al. The effect of Mendelian disease on human health: a measurement. *Amer J Med Genet* 1985; 21 : 231–42.

59   World Health Organization. *International classification of impairments, disabilities, and handicaps.* Geneva, 1980.

60   President's commission for the study of ethical problems in medicine and biomedical and behavioral research. *Screening and counselling for genetic conditions.* Washington, DC, US Government Printing Office, 1983.

Screening and Counselling

Report of Discussion Group

M. F. Niermeijer

The working group on genetic screening, counselling and genetic intervention recognized that genetic disease is one of a multitude of problems in health care. Globally, there are numerous other major issues, related to social and economic conditions, ranging from malnutrition to environmental pollution, which cause a much larger burden of disease. The size of the problem of genetic disorders, important as it is in itself, must be placed in this perspective.

A gradual development was seen in the meaning of "screening". Initially, the study of a large group of individuals was limited to studies in newborns (for metabolic diseases). Later, screening programmes involved the detection of disorders among adults also, such as cancer detection programmes. In the near future we may see the development of new forms of screening for the so-called common disorders, especially when DNA technologies become available for such a purpose.

In genetics, screening programmes for the detection and counselling of carriers of a number of autosomal recessive genes have been operating in several countries (for haemoglobinopathies, Tay Sachs disease, etc.). Some experiences of these programmes might provide the strategies applicable to larger screening programmes.

Recommendations

The working group formulated a number of recommendations:

(1) Participation in any screening programme is to be based upon a free and informed decision of the individual. This freedom of the individual in decision-making is the dominant principle in genetic screening and counselling. It applies to all types of genetic screening and counselling: either for an individual coming for counselling or for an individual tested in a screening programme or in a genetic diagnostic test. Moreover, the ethical environment of such a screening or counselling programme should be based upon the principles of beneficence, autonomy (autonomy involves, of course, full information on all aspects of the decision to be taken), confidentiality of data, and equity.

(2) Introduction of new technologies into a society necessitates information about their implications. This will be successful only if there is a framework of information and knowledge among the population. The working group suggests that education of the public, from school-age onward, both on genetics and prevention and on healthy lifestyles, is important to providing a sound basis for introducing new principles into a society.

(3) Also, scientists might be active in informing policymakers. An informed decision-making process by policymakers might be promoted by giving them information on the basic principles of genetics, and on new technologies or screening methods. The ethical problems involved in this particular area could be an integral part of this information and assist in decisions on health care allocation in the future.

(4) The development of predictive techniques (including DNA studies) for genetic diseases that have their onset later in life has accentuated an existing problem. Certain people may be identified by their family history or a family study or a genetic test as carriers of a genetic predisposition for a future disease or disability. They may experience some form of social handicap when this knowledge is used to exclude individuals from a job or life/disability insurance. The working group agreed that regulations for admission to either job or insurance must be developed in such a way as to prevent social crippling by loss of job or insurance because of any type of genetic information established in respect of an individual. The rationale for this proposal is the very rapid increase in the number of genetic markers for an increasing number of diseases. This could put a burden on an increasing number and groups of people. At the same time we should not forget that all human beings carry some three to ten deleterious genes, indicating that there is no justification for placing the burden on those individuals that can be identified by modern technology.

Areas of concern or reluctance

Besides these recommendations, the working group defined some areas where developments must be followed with concern or care, because more study or more ethical concern is needed, or because there are potentially undesirable developments.

Somatic-cell gene therapy for genetic disease involves the introduction of a normal gene into somatic cells (such as those of the bone marrow) for the treatment of certain genetic diseases. Its principles seem as justifiable as those of other therapeutic modalities, but its clinical application at this moment would seem premature. Much more data are needed on animal systems and on human *in vitro* cell-culture systems before a realistic perception of feasibility and safety can be made.

Genetic engineering of the germ line or the embryo is thought to have no place or no justifiable application. At this moment there are sufficient data on possible harmful effects, but insufficient methodology to monitor the embryo for undesirable side-effects.

Occupational screening of individuals for genetic susceptibility to hazardous substances or radiation in the working place is an area where one should be aware of discrimination in the work-force: everyone agrees that this should not prevent cleaning up the work-place. Also, there is concern about the limited predictive value of genetic susceptibility testing, because of the limited number of reliable tests available and the limited number of genetic traits known as indicators of genetic susceptibility.

The working group considers it a misuse of new genetic technologies to use chorionic villus sampling to make a diagnosis of sex in the eighth or tenth week of pregnancy. Since sex is no disease, the use of fetal diagnosis only for knowledge of fetal sex is to be discouraged, at least in European and American cultures.

The expansion of methodology to establish genetic information about an individual, and the potential social implications of such information, have corroborated the necessity of confidentiality of data in any type of genetic study. As a counterpart, counter-productive secrecy was noted in some areas in the biotechnology industry. Secrecy of data obtained during DNA research might interfere with the free research on human health problems and genetic disease. The working group considered that the development of a code of conduct might be an area for development here.

Areas for further development of actions, attitudes and policies

Both this and other working groups discussed the desirability of a study of the ethics of cost-benefit analysis. Such a study might be valuable for clarifying the interrelation of cost-benefit analysis and ethics. Also, it might look at the real goals that are aimed at in allocation studies. Would such a goal be longevity or quality of life? These goals are extremely different, especially in a moral sense, and would lead to very different conclusions.

Another area for development would be the ethics of abortion for late-onset genetic disorders (such as Huntington's disease, Alzheimer's disease, and more to come in the future). Similarly, these questions might be developed about those disorders where at present some form of medical therapy and intervention is possible, such as phenylketonuria, haemophilia and adrenal hyperplasia, and a number of others.

Stimulating the interaction between scientists, community, patient organizations, and policymakers is another area for development. Fears are raised that new technologies are introduced in society, resulting from regular exchanges between research workers, patient organizations and their communities; this might happen without control by, or information to, the government. Others fear that government and science might be working on strategies that might not be in the best interests of patients. The development of new strategies and their ethical implications for society would require optimal interaction of scientists, the community, patient organizations and policymakers.

During the rapid development and introduction of new genetic techniques a continuous awareness of the interrelation of science and society is essential if we are to avoid any undesirable implications in the field of eugenics. Quality control and verification of new methods of genetic diagnosis is another area that merits continuous attention.

Areas for support

In considering areas where active support might be possible, it seems that research support could be given to those types of predictive medicine where new or already available technologies are used to make a diagnosis of a disorder years prior to onset of clinical symptoms. Conditions for support would include such considerations as whether such programmes are aimed at the wellbeing of people or at testing either present or future technology. Moreover, such support is to be promoted for developing psychosocial support strategies in these programmes. These are essential to assist those who are going to be identified as affected or carrying a gene where the onset of a clinical disorder will be years later. The working-group discussions emphasized the need to establish the type and extent of psychosocial support in programmes actually in progress. This could help to establish needs in future similar programmes, allow allocation of resources, and also improve the acceptability of actual predictive diagnostic programmes.

In conclusion, the working group considered as dominant principles freedom and taking care of those to be counselled in research situations where the new technologies are applied at the frontiers of both human and technical development.

94

Organ Transplantation — Some Ethical Issues*

Francisco Vilardell**

Introduction

Since the demonstration by Alexis Carrel in the 'twenties of the feasibility of visceral implants[1] organ transplantation has become an important part of therapeutic medicine. The first successful kidney transplantation, between identical twins, was performed in 1954;[2] the first, much publicized, heart transplantation was undertaken in 1967;[3] the first liver transplantation took place in 1963;[4] the pancreas was transplanted in 1967[5] and the lungs and heart in 1969.[6] In general, the results of the early procedures were far from satisfactory because of transplant intolerance and rejection, surgical inexperience and possibly defective state of donor's organs. A crucial event has been the discovery and use of cyclosporin for the immunological treatment of recipients, which have considerably improved the outlook and long-term prognosis of most transplantation operations.[7] Corneal implantation, which began almost a century ago, has made steady progress thanks to the special characteristics and low antigenicity of the corneal tissue. Kidney transplantation has been established as a regular procedure, with sizeable cost-benefit advantages over continuous dialysis. Both heart and liver transplantation programmes are increasing in number in almost geometrical proportions. Both may prove of risk-benefit importance to some patients. Pancreatic transplantation, although somewhat less successful, has reached a reasonable level of success. Bone-marrow, bones, fascia, skin, and eardrums can be transplanted, and intestinal and single-lung transplantations are to be included among the new experimental procedures.

Thirty-nine countries have enacted laws on organ transplantation[8] and several well-documented studies on the legal aspects of transplantation have been published.[9, 10] In addition to the difficult technical, legal and scientific problems related to transplantation, many questions arise about the ethical relevance of the procedures involved, which have been answered only in a partial and uncertain way. Although there is a growing consensus that organ transplantation is not only morally permissible but even desirable and therefore should be encouraged,[11] important reservations have been voiced by representatives of some religious groups and cultures about the propriety of at least some of the

* The help of Mr S. S. Fluss, Chief, Health Legislation, WHO, in the preparation of this paper is gratefully acknowledged.
** Director, Escuela de Patologia Digestiva, Hospital de la Santa Cruz y San Pablo, Barcelona; President, CIOMS.

indispensable actions related to transplantation, such as organ retrieval or the definition of death.[12]

Organ Transplantation Today

Kidney

What can we expect from organ transplantation? Statistics on organ transplantation in the Western World are impressive. During 1984, 7 000 renal transplantations were performed in the United States of America and 7 700 in the European countries included in the Dialysis and Transplant Association (EDTA).[13] The reasons that kidney transplants lead the field are that they are technically much easier than the other procedures and that the patient can be very well prepared by the use of the artificial kidney.

Indications for transplantation continue to broaden, particularly in relation to the age of the patients admitted into dialysis programmes. Renal transplantation to selected patients up to the age of 70 years is technically and medically feasible; about 40% of new patients taken into dialysis are now over 55.[14] There would possibly be even more kidney transplants if nephrologists were to gain nothing from keeping patients on dialysis.[14] Graft survival after a kidney transplant depends on the nature of the donor. After transplantation of a kidney from a relative with identical Human Lymphocyte Antigen (HLA), the survival rate is more than 90%. The two-year graft survival rate may be as high as 83%[14] but is more often around 70%.[15]

Heart

By January 1985, 2 456 heart transplants had been done. Survival rates of the order of 80% have been reported, the attrition rate being somewhat more than for kidneys. A survival rate of 78% at five years has been reached.[16] By contrast, the average survival period for patients assessed as suitable for a transplant but dying while awaiting surgery is about nine months.[17]

Heart and Lung

Heart and lung transplantation remains an exceptional procedure owing in part to the difficulties in securing suitable donors, who should be anatomically matched, and in part to the limited time available for the transplant operation because of the low viability of the lung parenchyma. Actuarial survival rates at three years after operation may vary between 35 and 55%.[18]

Liver

There are now over 40 liver transplant centres in Europe and about 50 in the United States and Canada, and over 3 000 liver grafts have been performed.[19] In a leading institution, long-term survival rates in adults are 71% at one year and 67% at two years, and a 60% survival rate at five years is within reach.[20]

Pancreas

Technical problems have dogged pancreatic transplantation. Four reports of 50% one-year success rates have been published.[15] The best results were obtained in patients in whom simultaneous kidney and pancreatic transplants were undertaken; however, pancreatic transplantation still remains an experimental procedure.[21]

Bone-marrow

Over 9 000 marrow grafts have been performed, with a current annual increase of 2 500 new cases. Most are for leukaemia. Disease-free survival rates of 45 to 55% at three to five years can be achieved in leukaemic patients and the results may be even better in patients with severe thalassaemia.[22]

A great increase in the demand for transplants in all areas of medicine is to be expected in the next few years. Improved surgical techniques and progress in the treatment of immunological reactions will result in acceptable survival rates and consequently in cost- and risk-benefit outcomes favouring transplantation over current maintenance therapies in many conditions, widening its indications. Transplantation teams will probably come under pressure from patients, relatives and society at large to perform transplants irrespective of such factors as age of patient, cause of the disease or risk factors.[14] Non-observance of the criteria for selection of recipients and donors has been responsible for most of the early deaths after transplantation.[23]

Xenografts

By the early 'sixties it was felt that heterotransplantation, that is the use of grafts from other than the human species, might be a possible solution to scarcity of donors, by providing easy availability of organs. In all cases except the recent, much publicized transplant of a baboon heart to a neonate, conventional immunosuppression was used and resulted in poor graft and patient survival; however, one case of a renal xenograft surviving nine months provides a rationale for further investigations.[24] So far, a total of 18 kidneys, three livers and four hearts have been transplanted from non-human primates to man.[24] Heterotransplantation raises the moral question of the utilization of animals in such experimental therapies, an issue which has stirred important and so far unsettled controversies.[25]

Xenografts will probably be increasingly investigated if the number of possible donors continues to fall behind the number of possible recipients. In the distant future it may well be that with increasing numbers of transplantations the number of transplant failures that will cause patients to resume sustenance therapy or undergo retransplantation may equal the number of transplants that can be performed and hence compel further study of xenogenic transplantation.[13]

Implantation of Artificial Organs

The implantation of artificial organs has been the subject of serious studies in the past few years. The usefulness of kidney dialysis, which can maintain life for a very long time, is well established. Some patients, particularly those with terminal heart disease, cannot be expected to benefit from transplantation because of one or more contraindications. For these patients a permanent implantable cardiac assist or a total artificial heart may in the future offer a reasonable alternative. A total artificial heart was implanted for the first time in 1982, giving rise to multiple ethical questions, which have been excellently reviewed.[26] The main ethical problems are those related to informed consent (11 typewritten pages in the case of Dr Barney B. Clark) and the risk-benefit ratios of the implant procedures.[26]

Selection of Patients

Indications

Specific medical indications for transplantation are apparently not so easy to establish, since in many centres they are not identical (e.g., liver carcinoma patients accepted for transplantation in some units and refused in others); indications may vary also with the expertise of the team. Extrapolating from a rather opposite euthanasia model[27] one could probably advise transplantation "when prognosis for meaningful life is extremely poor or hopeless and further conservative treatment will be of no help". The indications may vary a great deal from severe heart or liver failure and impending death to primary biliary cirrhosis with unbearable pruritus and possibly a few additional years of relentless suffering.

Selection

Each potential recipient must be evaluated in terms of individual risk and benefit from the procedure. Criteria for acceptable candidacy are meant to be as objective as possible and subject to careful scrutiny so as to ensure that the graft will have maximum potential for saving the recipient's life. Probability of success seems to be the most widely used criterion for selection. This usually involves a range of medical and psychological criteria. However, the limits of medical care are not always clear: if one uses as a transplantation criterion a very short life-expectancy in patients who are very disabled, this may result in failure of the operation due to the poor condition of the patient. It has been said that the most dangerous period in the life of patients being assessed for transplantation is precisely the time prior to the intervention. Many deaths may occur while on the waiting list, usually more than in the post-operative period.[28] Besides the purely medical indications, other factors have no doubt played a role in the selection of patients for transplantation.

Age

Advanced age is, less and less, considered a contraindication to transplantation as total graft survival rates do not seem to be different from those of younger age groups.[29] Aged persons are increasingly accepted in kidney dialysis programmes and the number of aged patients on the waiting list for transplantation is bound to increase. Many find it improper to exclude any patient from treatment because of a date on the birth certificate.[30]

Inability to Cope with the Procedure

This may occur in the case of mental illness, specific psychological traits or severe physical handicaps.[31]

Lack of Support System

Lack of support for the person upon discharge from the hospital is a factor which many consider of critical importance[32] but which doctors cannot evaluate on their own.

Social Behaviour

Since transplant facilities are quite restricted in many areas, other factors have been analysed[33] which may influence selection, such as dependence on alcohol or drugs, which is usually considered a medical contraindication to transplantation. Yet there is much concern lest patients with these conditions are excluded not solely on the basis of clinical assessment.[34] Physicians will invoke the possibility that transplantation of the liver in a patient with a long history of alcohol dependence, for instance, has fewer chances of success because other organs are already damaged by alcohol and life expectancy is diminished, but this argument is not satisfactorily proven. A greater deterrent to transplantation might be that two out of three such patients in whom liver transplantation was successfully undertaken resumed drinking after some time![35]

Personal Criteria

Other criteria, such as the patient's importance to his immediate relations or his significance to society, have been advanced by some utilitarian thinkers. A discussion group during the XVIII CIOMS Conference could reach no consensus on any of these utilitarian principles because of difficulties in accepting quantification of values or in predicting any prospect of success. Agreement could not be obtained in deciding upon exclusion criteria, such as the case of a patient receiving a transplant as a consequence of self-inflicted disease, like alcoholic cirrhosis. Some philosophers, however, may find it ethically acceptable to exclude persons who through their own choices increase the cost of care.[36]

Ability to pay should not be an excluding factor, in the opinion of a majority. A recent report of the Task Force on Organ Transplantation of the US Department of Health and Human Services clearly stated that a patient's financial status should not limit the availability of the transplantation procedure.

The group further recommended that selection of patients for waiting-lists and allocation of organs be based on medical criteria, taking into account both need and probability of success. Otherwise, selection should be based on length of time on a waiting list, not on favouritism or other criteria.[37] Some moralists consider a waiting list to be equivalent to some sort of random selection or lottery, which they believe to be more equitable than other selection procedures.[38, 39] However, it is doubted that doctors select their patients for transplantation on strictly medical grounds. Some believe that transplantation criteria may disguise a judgement of social worth which is then presented as a medical decision.[34] Substantial discrepancies were found between 25 different renal units when a simulated selection of patients for transplantation was undertaken. Only one third of the patients would have been accepted by all units and no patient was rejected by all. It looks as though medical indications may be determined unconsciously by the available resources or perhaps by other personal factors that cannot be considered as strict medical issues.[29] This "medical" selection, of which patients may not be aware, may occur at any stage of the disease process, from the time when the general practitioner decides whether or not to send the patient to the hospital for study, for dialysis or transplantation, to admission to the intensive care unit, and evaluation by internists, psychiatrists, surgeons, etc. Will all these professionals assess equitably the medical risks of a 60-year-old Nobel Prize winner, the 18-year-old juvenile delinquent, the writer dependent on alcohol, the unemployed mother of several children and the rich foreigner who cannot have transplantation in his own country?

The Problem of Foreign Patients

Should foreign nationals be offered the same opportunities as a country's citizens? Several institutions take a sizeable number of foreign patients; this problem will no doubt be discussed at this meeting. The Task Force on Organ Transplantation[37] has recommended that non-immigrant aliens comprise no more than 10% of all kidney transplant recipients, and that no organs other than the kidney should be offered for transplantation unless no other suitable recipient can be found. The American Society of Transplant Surgeons has issued guidelines stressing the preferential treatment of native patients over foreign nationals, restricting the proportion of alien recipients to an average of 5%.[40] Ethical conflicts will probably arise in the future, particularly if transplantation is used as an emergency life-saving procedure. It will be difficult to deny an alien access to this treatment on the grounds that a quota has been filled.

Recipient's Consent

Patients' unwillingness is recognized as one of the principal obstacles to an increased transplantation rate.[13] The nature of informed consent may vary greatly with the type of intervention: whether it is a life-saving, emergency procedure with no alternative or an elective operation to improve quality of life. The patient should be told of the risks involved, the possibilities of success, the prospects for long-term survival, and the potential benefits in the quality of life. As Jonsen has aptly stated: "the value of rescue procedures derive from the quality of future life saved, not from the fact that death has been repelled".[41] Obviously, obtaining consent will be easier for well-established procedures, such as corneal or kidney transplantation. In the case of heart or liver substitution, where there is no other obvious alternative, the coercive nature of the patient's choice while on a waiting-list for a life-threatening procedure cannot be denied.

Consent may be more complicated if the transplantation technique is new. Its experimental nature should be frankly recognized and discussed; the difficulties inherent in telling a patient he is going to participate in an experiment of unknown benefits are great. In a much aired case of artificial heart transplantation, members of the ethical committee that reviewed the case doubted afterwards whether the patient was sufficiently satisfied with the quality of his life (he was never able to leave his bed after the operation).[26] The patient should always know that he can withhold consent at any time during the transplantation process.[42]

The informed-consent procedure should include a discussion of what is expected of the patient, namely compliance with the requirements of the procedure, such as permanent abstinence from alcohol or adherence to a strict life-regimen.[43]

Informed consent in the case of children raises many vexed questions. Children of a certain age will probably realize they are gravely ill, and will also have to face the emotional reactions of their families, who usually will argue strongly for transplantation. Should a child give consent to transplantation? A rule of thumb has developed that patients over the age of seven are to be taken seriously when they express assent or dissent.[43] Although the law authorizes parents, as the natural guardians, to give informed consent on behalf of their children they may not always act in the children's best interests, since they may be led by emotional but misguided attitudes. Quality of life is as important as survival itself: a short survival with prolonged suffering seems an unsatisfactory goal for a medical procedure. However, survival at whatever price seems to be what many parents desire, though the child might prefer a reasonable quality of life as a deciding factor. While kidney and liver transplants can save children's lives with a tolerable outcome, heart transplantation is still of doubtful risk-benefit value.[44] Very little is known about the predictable risks of transplantation in children of such unique organs as the heart and the liver, which may include further sources of pain and discomfort (biopsies to monitor rejection), limitation of freedom, and the psychological effects of trauma and separation from the parents. Other risks that may be discussed are a child's need of constant support, the possibility of developing personality problems, the risks to family stability if there are other children, and life-long expense. Whether Ronnie de Silvers, the seven-year-old boy who recently died while waiting for his fourth liver transplant, really wanted to go on, as his parents told the press, may be doubted.[45]

Live Donorship

Organ donations from living persons have been widely utilized for kidney transplants as well as for transplants of renewable tissues such as bone marrow. It is well proven that results of transplanting a kidney from an identical twin or a living relative have been consistently superior to those performed with cadaver organs. More than 30% of all kidney transplants in the United States are obtained from living donors.[46] It is claimed that the results of transplanting a kidney from any living donor are better than those of any cadaveric transplantation, because of the avoidance of complications secondary to the preservation of the transplanted graft.[46]

Generally, a patient can expect good graft function from a transplant from a close relative and this avoids having to wait a long time for a cadaver organ, and possibly saves the greater expense of continuous dialysis. Which family member should be asked to donate? A recent survey has shown that most members of the families felt that the mother should do so.[24] Should organs from living unrelated persons, even if "emotionally related", be used? It might seem reasonable to employ, in selected instances, donations from spouses or close relatives or even friends with an extreme interest in the patient's welfare. However, there are several objections:

(1) Removal of a kidney, in spite of statistical evidence that it is safe,[46] is not innocuous: around 20 donors have died;[47] evaluation of prospective donors includes invasive, possibly dangerous, procedures such as renal angiography;

(2) Undue pressure may be exerted on prospective donors, particularly in the case of transplantation of renewable tissues such as bone marrow, as a sort of "moral blackmail".[48]

(3) It is difficult to protect the identity of prospective donors whose names are stored in hospital computers; this problem could be obviated by creating a national registry of consenting organ-donors.[48]

(4) The recipient and the donor may feel special obligations to each other; anonymity should be assured, but it is difficult to do so.[49]

(5) A failed transplant may result in highly conflicting personal situations. In the United States alone 1 500 renal transplant recipients return to dialysis each year because they reject their grafts.[46]

(6) The right of the potential donor to refuse the organ for transplantation may not be respected by families, courts and the media.

(7) Living donations might open the way for commercialization.

Do persons "own" their bodies? In some countries, newspaper advertisements have offered organs for sale.[50] It has been reported that in India a kidney can be sold for $3 000 to $7 000; that in the Philippines prisoners have made donations in the hope of early parole; and that Japanese money-lenders, acting as modern Shylocks, permit debtors to repay them by authorizing them to sell a kidney.[51] Commercialism is not confined to such blatant cases; it may occur in much subtler ways, such as switching priorities in transplant waiting-lists, favouring patients who will pay large sums of money for the operation.[51]

Objections to any kind of commercialization have been widespread in the West, and almost all countries, including the United States of America[37] and the member countries of the Council of Europe,[52] prohibit the purchase of human organs for use in transplantation.

The Council of the Transplantation Society has elaborated stringent guidelines for the selection, protection and utilization of living donors:[53] unrelated living donors (not first-degree relatives) should be used only exceptionally; the motives of the donor must be truly altruistic and not self-serving or profit-making; active solicitation of living unrelated donors for profit is unacceptable; the living unrelated donor must satisfy the same ethical, medical and psychiatric criteria applied in the selection of related donors; no payments should be made to the donor, but reimbursement for expenses, loss of work, etc. related to the donation, is acceptable.

A possible solution that deserves further study has been advanced by Rapaport.[46] An international exchange of living-related donors and recipients could be organized on the basis of an exchange registry of emotionally related kidney-donors, whereby kidneys obtained from such a pool of intrafamilial incompatible donors could be used.

Cadaver Donorship: Definition of Death

There is no legal definition of death. We lack well-determined and uniform criteria for death.[54] Whether death is an "event" or a "process" is a matter of debate. Most definitions of death include not only the classical criterion of the irreversible cessation of respiration and heart beat (which, taken literally, would preclude organ sustenance by ventilation) but also a criterion of "brain death", a product of modern technology. This is usually defined as the "irreversible discontinuation of all brain functions including the brain stem". This definition allows for continuation of the heart beat and pulmonary ventilation, in order to keep the potential grafts in the best possible condition. Many guidelines have been published for the definition of brain death.[37, 55, 56, 57] Most include the dual alternatives as explained above. However, criteria of brain death are not universally accepted or applied, and differences in the interpretation of brain death may greatly complicate the obtaining of viable grafts. As recently as 1978 the Council of Europe decided not to issue any rules or criteria by which death could be ascertained, and left the decision to the established practice of the member states.[52] Most neurosurgeons accept the principle of brain death[58] and use the apnoea test as the final and probably most important clinical neurological examination of the brain stem because it provides reliable and rapid confirmation of brain death. Other elaborate tests (perfusion scintigraphy, etc) may be necessary if barbiturates, intoxicating drugs or hypothermia have been used.[59, 60]

There is considerable controversy as to whether "brain death" means the failure of the whole brain[61] as a sole criterion, or, as some would prefer, an "irreversible loss of consciousness and cognition",[62] on the ground that the latter criterion avoids the issue that the two criteria have different prognostic significance from the standpoint of other functions such as circulation (brain death *versus* the vegetative state). These criteria might perhaps help in the ethical analysis of decisions for organ harvesting from anencephalic babies, who die inevitably a few hours after birth because of lack of the forebrain, a structure necessary for characteristic human activity. Should anencephalic babies be considered as brain dead?[63] The concept that an anencephalic baby, because of the absence of brain development, has never been alive despite the presence of a heart beat is now accepted in the courts of the Federal Republic of Germany.[64] The concept "brain absent" has been formulated, and categorized with the "brain dead", which makes possible an earlier retrieval of organs.

No doubt the concept of brain death will continue to be an important theme for discussion in the coming years since there are still countries where it has not been accepted or legally recognized.[24]

Organ Procurement and Consent

In 1982, in the USA, out of some 20,000 potential donors — young or middle-aged patients classified as brain dead — only 2500 actually gave their organs.[65] There are many explanations of this depressing fact: lack of consent from relatives and other involved persons, technical difficulties with the procedure, contraindications to transplantation of the graft that were not evident during clinical evaluation, and the disturbing effects of organ retrieval surgery and pre-transplantation care of the donor on the staff of the intensive care unit and the operating room.

Ideally the donor should have given consent. Several ways of manifesting consent have been used, although none seems to be really satisfactory.[65] Donor cards, "living wills", and special marks on the driving licence are among the techniques that may help in obtaining donations. However, in many institutions, in spite of the evidence of the will to donate, the transplanting team requests family consent, perhaps for fear of legal problems. In at least 13 countries, policies of presumed consent ("contracting out") — the possibility of a donation unless the deceased person has expressly prohibited it in writing — have been enacted.[8] A policy of "required request" as advocated by Caplan,[65] the requirement that family members or guardians be given the opportunity to make a donation, is increasingly adopted by the American states and has already resulted in sizeable increases in the number of transplantations done at some centres.[66, 67] In the United States some difficult attempts have been made to procure organs from executed prisoners. They have met with an almost total lack of cooperation from the local authorities, mostly because of requirements for declaring the patient dead on the basis of heart death.[68]

Kidney procurement may be enhanced by the use of non-heart-beating donors, a technique used with partial success in the Netherlands.[69] However, it may be anticipated that, applying the strictest criteria, perhaps as many as 20% of transplant operations will not be completed, for technical reasons, particularly in the case of the liver.[70]

Many difficulties in obtaining consent have their origin in the attitudes of hospital staff. Many barriers seem to interfere with a request for a donation:[71] (1) lack of familiarity with the donation process; (2) legal factors; (3) personal feelings about organ donation, in part because staff may be reluctant to request it at a time of bereavement; (4) disturbing thoughts at having to resuscitate a patient who has been declared dead; (5) guilt feelings at consenting to the mutilation of a body of a person who until then had been treated intensively with the most advanced technology; (6) having to terminate support measures when the organs that required perfusion have been removed.[72] Physicians and nurses share these feelings to different degrees. Responsible nurses have recently made a plea to physicians to consult and collaborate with them in morally troublesome cases.[73] Close collaboration between all the personnel involved in these troublesome issues is essential, to improve the results of these life-saving efforts. Nurses not only may provide care to living and dead donors, but also are ideally placed to find potential donors.[32] Youngner[72] makes some proposals which might be of further help to the health team: (1) provide education; (2) recognize the legitimacy of emotional upset; (3) protect inexperienced and otherwise vulnerable staff; (4) show consideration for families; and (5) establish new rituals and practices appropriate for this new class of dead patients.

Follow-up of the "gift" by the members of the family of the donor is an extremely important issue in transplantation. Cadaver organ donation is often seen by next-of-kin as the highest form of charity. Most relatives will view donation as a positive aspect of death. They will want information about the fate of the organ and the outcome for the recipient.[74]

Religious and cultural beliefs will provide in many cases additional comfort, although in other instances they may forbid or complicate the transplantation procedure. Requests for organ donation should carefully review these important aspects before action. The request for organ donation may be better received from a trained requester who was not involved in the care of the deceased or affiliated with the transplant programme.[75]

105

Conclusions

This rapid and rather superficial survey permits only an introduction of an inventory of ethical issues that confront patients, institutions, the health care team, families and society in respect of transplantation. All the basic principles of medical ethics, beneficence, non-maleficence, autonomy and justice[76] influence the different aspects of the procedure, which may well be a paradigm of the interplay of these four fundamental doctrines. There are many different answers to most of these troublesome issues. Unfortunately, it appears that no one principle will resolve the difficult decisions for all. Answers to these questions may vary from one culture to another and from country to country. Each society has to decide what procedures are justified and for whom.[54] Meanwhile, it is hoped that with rapidly evolving technological progress some of the questions will gradually find answers that will merit more general acceptance.

References

[1] Cabrol, C. & Painvin, C.A. Organ transplantation (Preface). *Surg. Clin. North Am.* **66:** 437, 1986.

[2] Merrill, J.P. et al. Successful homotransplantation of human kidney between identical twins. *J.A.M.A.* **160:** 277, 1956.

[3] Barnard C.N. A human cardiac transplant. *S. Afr. Med. J.* **41:** 1271, 1967.

[4] Starzl T.E. et al. Evolution of liver transplantation. *Hepatology* 2: 614, 1982.

[5] Kelly W.D. et al. Allotransplantation of the pancreas and duodenum along with the kidney in diabetic nephropathy. *Surgery* **61:** 827, 1967.

[6] Cooley D.A. et al. Organ transplantation in advanced cardiopulmonary disease. *Ann. Thorac. Surg.* **8:** 30, 1969.

[7] Borel, J.F. et al. Biological effects of Cyclosporin: a new antilymphocytic agent. *Agents Actions* **6:** 468, 1976.

[8] Fluss, S.S. (Personal communication).

[9] Romeo Casabona, C.M. *Los Trasplantes de Organos.* Bosch, Barcelona, 1979.

[10] Australian Law Reform Commission's Report. *Human Tissue Transplants.* Australian Government Publishing Service, 1977.

[11] Pellegrino, E.D. Life, death and suffering from a Christian perspective. Their impact on health policy. In: Bankowski, Z. & Bryant, J.H. (eds), *Health Policy, Ethics and Human Values.* Geneva, Council for International Organizations of Medical Sciences, 1985, pp. 266–273.

[12] Sporken, P. *Die Sorge um den kranken Menschen.* Grundlagen einer neuen medizinischen Ethik, Patmos Verlag, Dusseldorf 1981: 232–239.

[13] Lundgren G. Widening indications of kidney transplantation — are there limits? *Transplant Proc.* **19:** 63, 1987.

[14] Castro L.A. Indications for renal transplantation — an introduction. *Transplant Proc.* **18:** 4 (Suppl 3) 5, 1986.

[15] Sheil, A.G.R. Clinical organ transplantation. *Transplant Proc.* **19:** 2782, 1987.

[16] Kemkes B.M. Introductory remarks to heart transplantation. *Transplant Proc.* **18:** 4 (Suppl 3) 25, 1986.

17 Jennet, B. *High Technology Medicine. Benefits and Burdens.* Oxford U.P., Oxford 1986: 111–115.
18 Primo, G. et al. Current indications and experience with heart-lung transplantation. *Transplant Proc.* **18:** 4 (Suppl 3) 41, 1986.
19 Pichmayer, R. et al. Liver transplantation. *Transplant Proc.* **19:** 103, 1987.
20 Hobbs, K.E.F. Liver transplantation. A review. *J. Hepatol.* **4:** 148, 1987.
21 Sells, R.A. & Brynger, H. Progress in pancreatic transplantation. *Lancet* **1:** 1024, 1987.
22 Lucarelli, G. et al. Marrow transplantation in patients with advanced thalassemia. *N. Engl. J. Med.* **316:** 1050, 1987.
23 Cabrol, C. et al. Heart and heart-lung transplantation. *Transplant Proc.* **19:** 88, 1987.
24 Margreiter, R. What can be done about the insufficient supply of grants? *Transplant Proc.* **19:** 79, 1987.
25 Kushner, T. & Belliotti, R. Baby Fae: a beastly business. *J. Med. Ethics* **11:** 178, 1985.
26 Wooley, F.R. Ethical issues in the implantation of the total artificial heart. *N. Engl. J. Med.* **310:** 292, 1984.
27 Beauchamp, T.L. & Childress, J.F. *Principles of Biomedical Ethics.* Oxford University Press, New York, 1979: 111.
28 Ghent C.N. Selection of patients. *Transplant Proc.* **18:** (Suppl 4) 160, 1986.
29 Roehl, L. et al. Renal transplantation in recipients aged over 50 years. *Transplant Proc.* **18:** 1012, 1986.
30 Brynger, H. et al. Renal transplantation in elderly patients. *Transplant Proc.* **18:** (Suppl 3) 12: 1986.
31 Parsons, V. & Lock, P. Triage and the patient with renal failure. *J. Med. Ethics* **6:** 173, 1980.
32 Doudera, A.E. Conference on legal and ethical issues surrounding organ transplantation. *Int. Digest Health Leg.* **37:** 154, 1986.
33 Van der Werff, A. Health policy, ethics and organ transplantation. In: *Health Policy, Ethics and Human Values.* Bankowski, Z. & Bryant, J.H. (eds) CIOMS, Geneva 1985: 206–216.
34 Atterbury, C.E. The alcoholic in the lifeboat. Should drinkers be candidates for liver transplantation? *J. Clin. Gastroenterol.* **8:** 1, 1986.
35 Calne, R. (Personal communication).
36 Englehardt, H.T. Jr. Allocating scarce medical resources and the availability of organ transplantation. *N. Engl. J. Med.* **311:** 66, 1984.
37 US Department of Health and Human Services. *Organ Transplantation Issues and Recommendations.* Report of the Task Force on Organ Transplantation. Washington DC, US Government Printing Office, April 1986.
38 Winslow, G.R. *Triage and Justice.* University of California Press, Berkeley, 1982.
39 Rescher, N. The allocation of exotic medical life-saving therapy. *Ethics* **79:** 173, 1969.
40 Monaco, A.P. Problems in transplantation — ethics, education and expansion. *Transplantation* **43:** 1, 1987.
41 Jonsen, A.R. On Baby Fae: Defining a Rescue Ethic. *International Herald Tribune* 31 Oct. 1984.
42 Parks, W.E. et al. Ethical aspects of transplantation. *Surg. Clin. North. Am.* **66:** 653, 1986.

43 Kanoti, G.A. Ethical considerations in solid organ pediatric transplants. *Transplant Proc.* **18:** (Suppl 2) 43, 1986.
44 Moskop, J.C. Organ transplantation in children: ethical issues. *J. Pediatrics* **110:** 175, 1987.
45 *Time.* May 11, 1987.
46 Rapaport, F.T. The case for a living emotionally related international kidney donor exchange registry. *Transplant Proc.* **18:** (Suppl 2) 5, 1986.
47 Starzl, T.E. Will live organ donations no longer be justified? *Hastings Center Report* (April) 5, 1986.
48 Caplan, A.L. Organ transplants: the cost of success. *Hastings Center Report* (Dec) 23, 1986.
49 Jameton, A.L. Organ donation: ethical issues. *Encyclopedia of Bio-Ethics* Vol. III, MacMillan and Free Press, New York, 1978: 1153.
50 Marcus C. Spectre of commercialism dominates transplant symposium. *Can. Med. Assoc. J.* **133:** 314, 1985.
51 Dickens, B.M. Legal and ethical issues in buying and selling organs. *Transplantation/Implantation Today* (Feb) 15, 1987.
52 Council of Europe. Harmonisation of legislations of member states relating to removal, grafting and transplantation of human substances. Strasbourg, 1978.
53 The Council of the Transplantation Society. Commercialization in transplantation. The problems and some guidelines for practice. *Transplantation* **41:** 1, 1986.
54 World Health Organization. *Human Organ Transplantation.* Report by the Director-General to the Executive Board. Seventy-ninth Session, 1986.
55 President's Commission for the Study of Ethical Problems in Medicine and Biomedical Behavioral Research. *Defining Death.* Washington DC, US Government Printing Office, 1982.
56 Working party on behalf of the Health Departments of Great Britain and Northern Ireland. *Cadaveric organs for transplantation. A code of practice including the diagnosis of brain death.* London, Her Majesty's Stationery Office, 1983.
57 Working party of the Pontifical Academy of Sciences. Report on artificial prolongation of life and the exact moment of death. *L'Osservatore Romano* (31 October) 1985.
58 King, A.B. Preliminary analysis of the size and characteristics of the donor pool in Northeastern Ohio and the influence of neurosurgeon's attitudes on the death process. *Transplant Proc.* **18:** (Suppl 2) 57, 1986.
59 Rohling, R. et al. Apnea test: pitfalls and correct handling. *Transplant. Proc.* **18:** 388, 1986.
60 Link, J. et al. Diagnosis of brain death by BAEP and CPS. Transplant Proc. **18:** 1985, 1986.
61 Bernat, J.L. et al. On the definition and criterion of death. *Ann. Intern. Med.* **94:** 389, 1981.
62 Youngner, S.J. & Bartlett, E.T. Human death and high technology: the failure of the whole brain formulations. *Ann. Intern. Med.* **99:** 252, 1983.
63 Harrison, M.R. Organ procurement for children: the anencephalic fetus a donor. *Lancet* **2:** 1383, 1986.
64 Holzgreve, W. et al. Kidney transplantation from anencephalic donors. *N. Engl. J. Med.* **316:** 1069, 1987.
65 Kolata, G. Organ shortage clouds new transplant era. *Science* **221:** 32–3, 1983.

66 Panel discussion on Organ Procurement. *Transplant Proc.* **18:** (Suppl 2) 61, 1986.
67 Oh, H.K. & Unieuski M.H. Enhancing organ recovery by initiation of required request within a major medical center. *Transplant Proc.* **18:** 426, 1986.
68 Meredith, J.H. Organ procurement from the executed. *Transplant Proc.* **18:** 406, 1986.
69 Ruers, T.J.M. et al. Non-heart beating donors: a successful contribution to organ procurement. *Transplant Proc.* **18:** 408, 1986.
70 Peters, T.G. et al. Liver procurement: lessons from the first sixty liver transplants at the University of Tennessee. *Transplant Proc.* **18:** 602, 1986.
71 Robinette M.A. et al. Barriers to organ donation within hospitals and involving health care professionals: findings of the Ontario Government Task Force on Kidney Donation. *Transplant Proc.* **18:** 387, 1986.
72 Youngner, S.J. et al. Psychosocial and ethical implications of organ retrieval. *New. Engl. J. Med.* **313:** 321, 1985.
73 Theis, E.C. Ethical issues. A nursing perspective. *New. Engl. J. Med.* **315:** 1222, 1986.
74 Bartucci, M.R. & Seller, M.C. Donor family responses to kidney recipient letters of thanks. *Transplant Proc.* **18:** 401, 1986.
75 Tolle, S.W. et al. Responsibilities of primary physicians in organ donation. *Ann. Intern. Med.* **106:** 740, 1987.
76 Gillon, R. *Philosophical Medical Ethics.* John Wiley, Chichester, 1986.

Transplantation Policies

A. van der Werff*

1. Background

Substitution of lost functions of the human body by various devices was one of the earliest technologies in medicine. The wooden leg, spectacles and the ear trumpet were antecedents of today's powered limb protheses, pacemarkers and artificial hearts. Transplantation of tissues or organs from people and animals represents a further step along the same path.[1] Human organ transplantation began with a series of experimental studies at the beginning of this century. Although blood transfusion was performed as early as 1918, and skin, bone and cornea transplants have been common for a long time, solid or vascularized organ transplantation in humans began only with the first kidney transplant performed between identical twins by Joseph Murray in 1954. Rapid progress was made with the development of drugs to suppress the immune responses and control rejection, and kidney transplantation was soon extended to living related donors other than twins and donors unrelated to the recipients. The key to the feasibility of kidney transplantation has been the development and implementation of kidney support systems (dialysis), which sustain life for patients with kidney failure. Simultaneous with the development in kidney transplantation, and making use of the advances in immunosuppressive drugs, the initial heart and liver transplants were performed. The first human liver was replaced by Thomas Starzl in 1963, and in 1967 the first human heart transplant was carried out by Christian Barnard. These events gave rise to an initial enthusiastic wave of organ transplants, which was initially not sustained, because of discouraging clinical results. Today the World Health Organization (WHO) is able to report that advances in immunosuppressive therapy, better surgical methods including microvascular anastomosis, organ procurement, preservation techniques and post-operative care regimens in the last ten years have had a major impact on both safety and efficacy of organ transplantation. In its report WHO concludes that now kidney transplantation is a standard treatment for irreversible renal failure, and both heart and liver transplantation are accepted methods for treating end-stage diseases of these organs. WHO also makes the observation that many questions about organ transplantation remain unanswered.[2]

Since heart and liver transplants are no longer experimental treatments this cannot be used as a reason for withholding them. However, ethical and economic issues related to this type of advanced technology cannot be ignored. Medical history shows that as soon as a new effective

---

* Consultant, Ministry of Welfare, Health, and Cultural Affairs, Rijswijk, Netherlands.

method of treatment is developed it is difficult to deny its use when needed.

Organ transplantation inevitably attracts attention because it is life-saving or life-enhancing and it is costly. Also, it raises ethical issues about the procurement of organs and about the balance between burdens and benefits for the patient who receives a donor's organ. Transplantation is particularly important to the public. It is a basic requirement that the donation of organs and tissues by the public be voluntary. The public therefore has rightly claimed a role in decisions regarding developing and implementing transplantation policies and practices. Thanks to the media there is now keen public interest in the technicalities, the economies and the personal dramas associated with transplantation — as well as with its effect on other activities of health care that compete for limited resources.

In discussing these questions I have concentrated on organ transplantation therapies for patients with life-threatening deficiences of kidney, liver and heart functions, because these transplants raise the most difficult questions, and are the more expensive forms of transplant.

2. The Present State and Future Development of Organ Transplantation

2.1 Summary of Organ Transplantation and Outcome

The increased effectiveness of organ transplants has stimulated the increase in the number of transplant procedures. Heart and liver transplantation has lagged behind kidney transplantation as regards widespread application. The strict limits on the length of time that the heart or liver can be preserved after removal from the cadaver donor and the more stringent requirements for the cadaver donor have restrained the development of these transplants. However, a major constraint on heart and liver transplantation has been its cost. Below an impression is given of the magnitude of the total activity in Europe and North America:[3]

	First transplant performed in:	Estimated accumulated number of transplants up to 1985 inclusive:
Kidney	1955	150 000
Heart	1967	2 700
Liver	1963	2 200

The numbers of heart and liver transplants have increased dramatically in the last few years. In 1985 1 010 heart transplants were performed, or almost 40% of the accumulated total from 1967 onwards, and in 1986, as many as 1 415. In the last two years, therefore, 60% of the total took place. The same can be said of liver transplantation. Of an accumulated total up to 1985 of 2 200 liver transplants 830 were performed in the last year (in USA 602 and in Europe 228), i.e. 40%. With the growth in numbers has come also increases in survival rates, owing mainly to advances in immunosuppressive therapy. For 1985 the leading transplant centres in Europe and North America could report one-year survival rates of 90–97% for kidney,[4] 80–85% for heart, and 60–70% for liver transplantation.

Also, the number of transplant centres in the USA and Europe[3] increased between 1981 and 1985 from 15 to 101 for the heart and from 4 to 71 for the liver.

There is wide variation in the number of transplants performed at different centres. Many centres perform rather few and this may be having the effects of excessive diffusion of expertise and experience, ineffective use of scarce organs, and unduly high costs.[5]

2.2 Kidney Transplantation

End-stage renal disease occurs in Europe and North America with an annual incidence of approximately 70 cases per million population. The number treated by renal transplant varies in different countries from 15 to 45 per million, thus meeting about half the theoretical need. The survival rate for transplant recipients now exceeds that for patients treated with renal dialysis. Transplant patients also achieve a degree of rehabilitation and a quality of life that no other form of therapy can provide. Most large transplant centres can report one-year survival rates of about 90–95% after cadaveric renal transplant and about 97–98% after a transplant from a living family donor. It is not expected that the overall rate will further improve.[6] In Europe the treatment is paid for from general taxation or social security funds. There are essentially no financial barriers to kidney transplantation, therefore. In the USA, health care is basically private, with the exception of Medicare and Medicaid. The funding for end-stage renal disease is, however, unique, since the US Government established in 1972 the End-Stage Renal Disease (ESRD) Program, which entitles eligible beneficiaries to payment through Medicare for dialysis and kidney transplantation. Medicaid and the private insurers followed suit, and from the mid-'seventies onwards dialysis and kidney transplantation became widely available to practically all residents of the USA. regardless of their ability to pay.

2.3 Heart Transplantation

Great advances in clinical application of the heart transplant have been made during the past decade. It is now an established treatment of patients suffering from end-stage heart disease with a poor prognosis for survival beyond 6 to 12 months. During the past three years there has been an unprecedented degree of activity in this field, owing largely to the consistently good results achieved by the heart transplantation team at Stanford University and the availability of cyclosporine therapy. Actuarial survival rates after transplantation are now within the reach of 80–85% at one year. Rehabilitation — defined as patients' ability to live and function as they did before their illness — has been achieved in over

85% of the long-term survivors.[6] A major difficulty still is organ procurement and transport of organs to distant recipients because of the short time (four hours) for which the heart may be preserved. In Europe heart transplants are performed almost exclusively in university hospitals. Since no private hospitals are involved, patients pay only a small amount of the total costs of the operation. However, most European governments are controlling the activity for economic reasons. In the USA there are serious financial barriers to heart transplantation. There are no federal programmes for reimbursement. Some states have established public reimbursement programmes. Private insurers provide coverage for eligible participants.

2.4 Liver Transplantation

Liver transplantation is now an accepted therapy for congenital diseases in children and for selected acquired diseases in adults. Overall survival rates after liver transplantation vary from centre to centre and depend mainly on the selection of patients. The largest number of transplants have been performed in Pittsburgh, USA, by the Starzl-team: 668 by the end of 1985 and 272 during that year. Starzl and his associates have classified their survival statistics under pre-CsA and post-CsA eras. In the post-CsA category the overall one-year survival rate was 70%, with better results in children than in adults.[6] The shortage of donor organs, particularly from children, is a serious impediment to widespread use of liver transplantation as the treatment for end-stage liver diseases. Organs can be preserved for 8 to 10 hours, but long-range organ transportation, as well as thorough donor evaluation and preparation of recipient, are limited by this restriction. Economic factors undoubtedly have contributed to the slower rate of diffusion of liver transplantation in Europe as compared with the USA. In Europe, like heart transplants, liver transplants are performed almost exclusively in university hospitals. Liver transplants are considered as one of the most difficult and demanding procedures in surgery, and, if the costs are calculated from first referral until discharge of the patient, they are very high. For this reason several European countries still restrict the numbers of transplants and budgets. In the USA financial barriers exist for nearly all adults seeking liver transplants. Public programmes at both the federal and state levels provide for only a few paediatric patients. Private insurers also include coverage, but only for eligible participants.

2.5 Organ Transplant Technology in the Year 2000

The rapid development and expansion of organ transplant technology in the past few years is expected to continue in the next 15 years. A recent international study on the future of health care technology requested by the Dutch Government[7] projects substantial improvements of current technologies, such as renal dialysis, kidney transplant, heart transplant, and artificial hip and knee joints. New technologies could profoundly alter the scene. With advances in the field of immunosuppressive drugs and growing understanding of immune system functioning, such organs

114

and tissues as pancreas, bone, small bowel, and endocrine organs could be transplanted successfully. Total body irradiation (as is currently done prior to bone-marrow transplantation) may be used for additional types of transplant. Irradiation of the lymph nodes and spleen may become an important adjunct to transplant, and would be associated with less radiation than total body irradiation. Experimental technologies such as the artificial heart, artificial pancreas, shoulder joint replacement, and cochlear implants may become commonplace. Prosthetics and robotics could become far more sophisticated, through combining the advanced knowledge in materials science with that concerning foreign body reaction, computer control and miniaturization, knowledge of nerve and muscle control, and knowledge of the dynamics of human movement.

2.6 The Widening Gap Between the Need for Organs and the Supply of Donors

An overriding problem common to all organ transplantation pro-grammes as well as in tissue banking (for corneal, skin and bone transplantation) is the widening gap between the need for the organs and tissues and the supply of donors. Despite substantial support for transplantation and a general willingness amongst people to donate organs and tissues after death, demand far exceeds supply. The increasing gap between demand and supply can clearly be demonstrated by the figures presented by EUROTRANSPLANT on kidneys:[8]

	1980	1982	1984	1985	1986
Total waiting-list:	2 865	3 756	5 285	6 605	7 360
Total transplanted:	1 231	1 493	2 065	1 984	2 470

3. Determinants of Transplant Policies

3.1 The Framework for Policy Development

Health policymakers have to consider a wide range of topics related to organ procurement and transplantation. Medical, social, ethical, techni-cal, organizational, economic and legal aspects will have to be analysed for policy development. Transplant policies concern organ donation and procurement, the organization and structure of organ procurement including organ sharing, patient access and payment for organ transplan-tation, and diffusion and adoption of transplantation technology. Transplant policies may result in legislation. Although these issues are universal, transplant policies may differ from country to country, because of differences in the sociopolitical and political-administrative determinants of policymaking. National policies have to be coordinated since many medical, technical, ethical, organizational and legal aspects of organ procurement and transplantation go beyond the boundaries of individual (national) states. The Council for International Organizations of Medical Sciences (CIOMS) was one of the first international organizations to participate actively in the international debate (1968).[9] At the political-administrative level the Council of Europe is promoting the harmonization of legislation relating to removal, grafting and transplantation of human substances (1978).[10]

3.2 Organ Donation and Religious Traditions

The donation of organs is more complex than is often recognized and its connection with major moral and religious beliefs is significant. The Christian tradition no longer occupies an official regulative position in Western life and culture but Christianity remains a major institution in the West, with significance for millions. Its position on the subject can influence greatly the acceptance of a system of organ and tissue retrieval. In a 1985 Gallup poll, 9% of respondents indicated that organ transplantation was against their religion and 12% referred to their belief in the resurrection of the body as one reason for their unwillingness to donate organs.[11] Also, the opposition to organ transplantation among such minority groups as Orthodox Jews, Christian Scientists and some Protestant sects cannot be ignored. The Christian and Jewish traditions emphasize the 'embodied self', rather than a sharp dualism between 'spirit' and 'body'.[12] This emphasis supports a principle of respect for persons that is not limited to their (disembodied) spirits but also includes their bodies, both before and after death. Jewish law prohibits deriving benefit from, mutilating, or delaying the burial of a corpse, but this prohibition can be overridden to save a life. In general, Judaism recognizes the right to donate bodily parts, emphasizing that the death of the donor must be definitely established. Both Roman Catholics and Protestants tend to support organ donation, believing that God's power to resurrect the body will not be thwarted by prior disposal of its parts. Christian ethics provides positive warrants for the act of giving. In matters so fundamental as the donation of human organs, giving and receiving are better than routine taking and getting, and are certainly to be preferred to buying and selling. However, even though these religious traditions tend to permit, and even to praise, 'giving to save the life of his or her neighbour' these views cannot generally be interpreted as an obligation of post-mortem organ donation.

3.3 Policies and Ethical Values

Transplant policies should increase the supply of organs and tissues and thus produce the greatest good for the greatest number without violating other important ethical principles and values. Policy development in organ transplantation should be directed largely towards its major goal, i.e., saving lives and improving the quality of life. The report of the Hastings Center on this subject (1985) recommended the development of policies that not only contribute to an increase in the number of cadaver organs obtained for transplant, but also acknowledge and advance the moral values and concerns of society regarding individual autonomy and privacy, the importance of the family, the dignity of the body, and the value of social practices that enhance and strengthen altruism and sense of community.[13] The US Task Force on Organ Transplantation agreed with this statement and concluded 'that any proposed policy that disregards these values can be expected to arouse vigorous and widespread opposition'.[14]

To be able to make choices and to balance efficiency and effectiveness of policies against societal values, it has been suggested to distinguish ethical acceptability, ethical preferability and political feasibility. Within the range of ethically acceptable policies, some may be ethically preferable and politically feasible and others not. Judgments about ethical acceptability and preferability involve the whole range of moral principles and values that have been identified.[15]

4. Policies to Increase the Supply of Organs

4.1 Policy Alternatives

The consequences of the critical shortage of organs are often fatal for those who need them. Many patients are dying in both Europe and North America while awaiting a new kidney, heart or liver. Options for policies to increase the supply of organs range from a system of voluntary donation (informed consent), required request, or presumed consent, to tax credits and the creation of a market in cadaver organs. For kidneys, living persons can be used as donors. Artificial organs could solve some of the problems that result from the scarcity of human organs. Also animals are possible sources of organs.

4.2 The System of Voluntary Donation (Informed Consent)

The system of voluntary donation requires approval of the donor, i.e., the expressed consent of the deceased. If such consent is not available, the organs cannot be removed from the body. In a broader version of this system family members have the right to decide whether to donate organs in the absence of a direction from the deceased. If no family can be located, those with legal or moral responsibility for the body may consent to organ donation. This system of voluntary donation and consent is applied in the USA in all states on the basis of the Uniform Anatomical Act (1968). A minority of European countries practise also a system of informed consent, sometimes without a specific legal basis (Federal Republic of Germany, the Netherlands and Ireland). The United Kingdom and Switzerland, however, have a legal basis; they apply an extended version of uninformed consent — if on inquiry no reasons can be found that the deceased, the legal representative or family would object, consent is presumed.

Donor cards play a minor role. Only relatively few people carry them. They are seldom found at the scene of a fatal accident or brought to the attention of physicians and families. Although signed donor cards constitute legally effective consent, physicians are reluctant to retrieve organs on the basis of the cards alone, and almost always require the consent of the next-of-kin. Another possibility to help increase the supply of organs is the establishment of a national registry, i.e., a computerized list of individuals who have indicated their willingness to be donors and who have agreed to be listed on a registry so that their wishes can be honoured at the time of death.

4.3 Required Request

The voluntary donation system could be improved by routine inquiry.[16] A major problem with the voluntary system is that families are not informed of their option to donate organs after brain death is determined. Routine inquiry would require hospitals to establish a system to ensure that the next-of-kin of all suitable donors are offered the opportunity of donating organs. Routine inquiry policies are necessary because health professionals (including nurses) are generally reluctant to discuss the possibility of donation of organs and tissues with families facing the death of a loved one, and because family members fail to remember this option in their time of grief. Routine inquiry places the responsibility for offering the family the option of organ donation on the institution, rather than on a particular staff member. Trained health professionals should discuss organ donation with families of all deceased patients who are suitable candidates for organ donation or should refer the patient to a regional organ procurement organization, so that a procurement co-ordinator will have an opportunity to approach the family. This concept receives general support in the USA.

4.4 Presumed Consent

Presumed consent grants health personnel the authority to remove organs from cadavers for transplantation whenever usable organs are available at the time of death in the absence of objection from the deceased or family members. Presumed consent places the burden of opting out of organ donation on those who object to this procedure rather than, as is the case under the system of informed consent, upon those who wish to opt for organ donation. In many European countries this system is legally applied, viz. Austria, Belgium, Denmark, Finland, France, Greece, Italy, Luxembourg, Norway, Portugal, Spain, Sweden and Turkey. This system has several variants, but the differences are small. In some countries, e.g., Denmark and Sweden, the relatives have to be notified in spite of the presumed consent, to avoid the removal of organs before the next-of-kin are informed of the death. In some countries, e.g., France, doctors are not willing to remove organs from cadavers without the consent of family members, despite the adopted public policy allowing strong presumed consent. In practice, physicians find it psychologically intolerable to remove organs from a body without obtaining the permission of the next-of-kin. The system of presumed consent may be extended by a national (central) registry for recording objections. Such a registry has recently been introduced in Belgium (1986).

118

4.5 The Sale of Organs

One possible public policy alternative is a market in cadaver organs (kidneys). Commercialization of organ procurement was recently debated in the USA (1985) and in the World Health Assembly (May 1987). In the USA the National Organ Transplant Act of 1984 prohibits the transfer of 'any human organ for valuable consideration if the transfer affects interstate commerce'. However several abuses have been reported in recent years: exporting and selling cadaveric kidneys abroad; advertising for non-immigrant aliens to receive transplants in the USA without regard to established waiting-lists and medical criteria; brokering kidneys from living unrelated donors; and selling organs within the country.[17] Advocates of the sale of organs argue that a market would respect the freedom of individuals to do what they want to do with their lives as long as they do not harm others. Opponents emphasize that individuals are not acting freely but are being exploited when they dispose of their bodily parts in a commercial transaction. Payment would cause undesirable encouragement of donation from persons who are poor or unhealthy. It could also cause deterioration in standards of testing, with increased risk to recipients. Some opponents assert that traffic in 'human spare parts' is objectionable in itself, and that payment would encourage blackmail, coercion or even killing. In general, society's moral values militate against regarding the body as a commodity. On these arguments the sale of organs is rejected, in both the USA and Europe. The law should forbid payment of any kind to any person for human organs or tissues removed from any living person or any dead body.

4.6 Tax Credits

To close the gap between the need and the supply of organs proposals have been made to provide income and estate-tax deductions in respect of prospective and deceased donors. For many, such indirect incentives may be more acceptable than direct payments. However, it is important to consider not only their effectiveness and efficiency but also how they really differ, if at all, from direct payments. It is, in particular, difficult to draw the line between direct payments and coverage of a donor's medical expenses, compensation of a living donor's lost wages, and payment of the burial expenses of a deceased donor. If the line could be drawn in a satisfactory way, some objections to a policy of tax credits might decline. However, such a policy would benefit the middle and upper classes, not the poor, and might be objectionable on this ground.[18]

4.7 Live Organ Donations

For kidneys and renewable tissue such as bone marrow and blood, living persons can be used as donors. In contrast to Europe, the USA still obtains approximately 25% of its transplanted kidneys from living donors. For years physicians and ethicists have argued over the relative risks and benefits of soliciting kidney donations from living relatives. On the negative side of the ethical equation are the emotional pressures on family members and possible uses of coercion and persuasion. On the positive side have been arguments about the benefits to the donor of being allowed to give such a precious gift and to help others. But support for using living donors has rested on the clinical evidence that these transplants were more successful. Today this may be no longer the case. It would be premature to stop asking living relatives to donate organs, considering the severe shortage in supply. But, knowing what we know now, asks Starzl, should we go on encouraging living relatives to provide organs — taking whatever risks this entails — when families of brain-dead people may never be asked whether they wish to donate their dead relatives' organs? Is it ethical to harm the living before harvesting the dead?[19]

4.8 Substitutes for Human Organs

Artificial organs could solve some of the problems that result from the scarcity of human organs for transplantation. Animals are another source.

Artificial Organs

Transplantation of organs such as kidney, heart and liver may well be a passing phase in medical technology until alternative means of substituting lost functions are found. While kidney analysis is an accepted and widespread 'support system', the artificial heart is more debatable.

The total artificial heart with which there has been the most clinical experience is the Jarvik-7. This device represents the culmination of decades of work by Willem Kolff, recently with Donald Olson and Robert Jarvik, and the surgical experience of William de Vries and his associates. Between October 24, 1985 and July 31, 1986, the Jarvik-7 total artificial heart was implanted into six moribund patients in an attempt to test its potential as a bridge from almost certain death to cardiac transplantation. It is reported that four of these patients are now well and at home after implementation of the device and subsequent cardiac transplantation. The results of this trial indicate that, in properly selected cases, direct benefit to the patient can be obtained as a bridge to transplantation.[20] This experience has provided important information that should lead to improvement of the support device. However, we cannot expect that the artificial heart will substitute for human donor hearts as a permanent solution, at least not in the foreseeable future.

Animal-to-Human Transplants

Although experimental animal-to-human transplants were performed in the early 'sixties, they were generally abandoned until late October 1984, when 'Baby Fae' received the first baboon heart. It seems to be generally agreed that science went too far in this case.[21] Animal-to-human transplants should rather be considered as a last resort. Although the moral objection to the sacrifice of animals should be taken seriously, most people believe that it is outweighed if there is a significant chance

120

of extending human life or of reducing pain and suffering. A taboo on interspecies transplantation need not be maintained, but, in general, extreme caution is required in the use of animal organs while laboratory and animal research continues.

4.9 Changing the Attitudes of the Public and Health Professionals

Public Attitudes

The 1985 Gallup poll in the USA is a rich source of information on the attitudes of the public. Experiences in Europe are similar. The Gallup poll reported that 93% of the Americans surveyed knew about organ transplantation and, of these, 75% approved of the concept of organ donation. Nevertheless, only 27% indicated that they would be very likely to donate their own organs, and only 17% had completed donor cards. Of those who are very likely to donate, nearly half have not told family members of their wish, even though family permission is usually requested before an organ is removed. The fears and misconceptions that are barriers to organ transplantation are listed in descending order of importance:

- They might do something to me before I am really dead
- Doctors might hasten my death
- I don't like to think about dying
- I don't like someone cutting me up after I die
- Never thought about it
- Family might object
- Against my religion
- Complicated to give permission[22]

Attitudes of Health Professionals

Physicians and nurses who care for patients dying in hospitals can exercise a 'gatekeeper' function of identifying potential donors and raising the issue of donation with families. Physicians are in a position to facilitate organ donation but too frequently do not. This is the major reason that the US Task Force on Organ Transplantation recommended that routine inquiry policies be adopted. The attitudes of health professionals can be attributed to many factors:

- Lack of knowledge of the need for organ and tissue donors
- Lack of awareness of the success and cost-effectiveness of transplants
- Lack of knowledge about brain death and how to identify a potential donor
- Reluctance to discuss organ donation with potential donor families
- Reluctance on the part of physicians to ask something of the family when they were unable to save the patient
- Lack of time[23]

Education

In the final analysis one may conclude that the gap between the need for organs and the supply of donors can be closed only if the attitudes of the public and health professionals with respect to organ donation and procurement can be changed. Their education in this respect is the best means of doing so and is undoubtedly highly preferable ethically to any other means. Although expensive, it is likely to be politically acceptable in all countries.

5. The Organization and Structure of Organ Procurement

When kidney transplantation became an effective form of therapy in the 1960s, it was necessary to develop systems for procuring organs from cadavers. In both Europe and North America organized programmes to increase the availability of post-mortem organs were established.

In Europe these organizations are centralized at supranational or national level, whereas the USA has a large number of independent, locally-based organ procurement agencies. The European organ-sharing organizations are: Eurotransplant (Austria, Belgium, Federal Republic of Germany, Luxembourg and The Netherlands), Scandia Transplant (Denmark, Finland, Norway and Sweden), UK Transplant (England and Ireland), France Transplant (France, Switzerland and Spain), Luso Transplant (Portugal), Hispano Transplant (Spain), Swiss Transplant (Switzerland), and North Italy Transplant (which serves northern Italy and two regional coordination centres, in Milan and Rome).

The USA, in 1984, had approximately 100 organ procurement agencies. The long-range goal is to gradually develop a unified national network of organ-sharing; it would encompass patient registry, coordinate organ allocation and distribution, and apply standard procedures and mechanisms with respect to governance, organ procurement and information processing.

Organizations of organ procurement aim first at matching available donor organs with the most suitable recipients. To achieve this, an organizational network is established and procedures and mechanisms are developed to support the entire process from donor procurement to the transplant operation. In this activity organ procurement organizations act as collaboration centres with all those involved in the transplant process throughout the health services system, i.e., donors and recipients, physicians, institutions and transplant centres. Organ procurement organizations coordinate organ allocation and distribution based on an agreed system of organ-sharing. A computerized, up-to-date waiting-list of potential transplant patients is at the centre of the activities. To realize the best possible donor-recipient match, a refined, computer-based system of blood and tissue typing (histocompatibility matching or HLA typing) is available.

To achieve a scale that is large enough to be able to treat all cases and special categories of patients, interregional, interstate, national, and (in Europe) international cooperation may be necessary. From an ethical point of view the aim should be to miss no opportunity to organize organ procurement on such a scale and in such a manner that at least patients in urgent need can receive organs so that they can live. Networks of sufficient size and organization could solve specific problems in transplantation, such as the accumulation of patients on waiting-lists; also, they could provide specific categories of patients, such as small children, with an expanded opportunity to receive a transplant. The ability to match donors and potential recipients would be enhanced, and the outcome of organ transplantation improved.

6. Equity in Organ Transplantation

6.1 Patient Selection

Even with the best policies for, and organization of, organ procurement, organs are likely to remain scarce, and problems of access and allocation will continue to require public policies. The supply of donor organs is limited, and only a restricted number of people can receive a transplant in a particular year. Increasingly, transplant recipients must be selected from a large pool of patients who need this procedure. Transplantation teams set the criteria for patient selection, and organ procurement organizations use these criteria to assist in the placement of organs. As scarce, life-saving resources, donated organs should be used in a way that assures good patient and graft survival rates and an acceptable length and quality of life. This requires an effective, efficient, and 'objective' fair method of distributing organs. The organization of organ procurement described in the preceding section would meet these criteria. Donated organs belong to the public; decisions with respect to the selection of patients should therefore be based on criteria that are publicly stated and can be publicly defended. It is ethically preferable that these selection criteria are not based on morally irrelevant characteristics, such as sex or race. There is general agreement in both Europe and the USA to use broad medical criteria to establish the waiting-list and then to use narrower medical criteria to determine who should actually receive the organ that becomes available.

6.2 Access and Ability to Pay

As indicated before, in Europe the cost of kidney transplants is largely covered by public insurance or by government budgets from general taxation. In the USA virtually all kidney transplants are paid for by Medicare, Medicaid, or private insurance, although the expensive immunosuppressant therapies are not covered. Medicare also pays for liver transplants for eligible children under 18 years. In Europe, the costs of heart and liver transplants are generally covered from public funds, but the number of procedures is restricted in many countries for budgetary reasons, or because these transplants are still considered experimental, or for a combination of these reasons. In the USA, only the wealthy or those who can raise sufficient funds through public appeals can receive a heart or liver transplant. There is no equity for all patients in access to and payment for organ transplantation in the Western world. But should there be equity? The US Task Force on Organ Transplantation recommended that donated organs indeed should be distributed to medically eligible recipients regardless of their ability to pay for the transplant.[24] This view would also be acceptable in the national insurance system of Canada and is fully in line with the concept of 'solidarity', upon which the insurance and other financing systems of most European countries are based. Despite its high cost, it is justified to aim at equity in lifesaving and life-enhancing organ transplantation. This view is supported by three arguments. First, a number of lifesaving organ transplants, such as heart and liver transplants, are neither experimental nor unproven; they produce outcomes in terms of longevity and quality of life that are equivalent to treatments that are covered by insurance or government budgets. Secondly, since all countries in the Western world, including the USA, have rejected wealth discrimination in end-stage renal disease, it would be fair to extend this commitment to other organ transplants that are also accepted methods for treating end-stage diseases of these organs. The third argument is directly related to organ transplantation. It is unfair and even exploitative for society to ask people to donate organs if these organs will then be distributed on the basis of ability to pay. This argument connects organ procurement with organ distribution and focuses attention on the very nature of the gift of a donated organ. Organs are a public resource, and all members of the public who need a transplant should have equal access to them. This argument offers an independent justification for the societal funding of organ transplants, without building on a general right to health care or on what society already offers. Governments, as representatives of the public, have the responsibility to develop and implement policies, and prepare legislation which guarantees a sufficient supply of organs and fair distribution to medically eligible recipients on the basis of equity.

References

1   Jennet, B. Implants, Transplants and Artificial Organs, Technical Feasibility versus Social Desirability, *Int. J. of Technology Assessment in Health Care*, **2**: 365–68 (1986).
2   World Health Organization *Human Organ Transplantation*, Report by the Director-General, EB 79/8, Geneva, 1986.
3   Sources: *Organ Transplantation, Issues and Recommendations*, Report of the Task Force on Organ Transplantation, US Department of Health & Human Services, Rockville, 1986; 7th Congress of the International Society

for Heart Transplantation (ISHT), New Orleans, 5–7 March 1987; and Höckerstedt, Kand Kankaanpää, J.: Liver Transplantation in Europe — Present Status, *Int. J. of Technology Assessment in Health Care*, **2**: 451–63 (1986).

4 US Department of Health & Human Services, Health Care Financing Administration: End-Stage Renal Disease Program, Medical Information System, Facility Survey Tables, 1984.

5 Evans, R.W. The Heart Transplant Dilemma. *Issues in Science and Technology*, 1986.

6 World Health Organization, *Human Organ Transplantation*, Report by the Director-General, EB 79/8, Geneva, 1986.

7 Scenario Commission on Future Health Care Technology, Banta, H.D. *Anticipating and Assessing Health Care Technology*, Vol. 1, Martinus Nijhoff Publishers, Dordrecht, 1987.

8 Eurotransplant Foundation: Annual Report 1985, Leiden, 1986.

9 CIOMS. *Heart Transplantation*, Report of the Second Round Table Conference. CIOMS, Geneva, 1968.

10 Council of Europe: *Harmonization of Legislations of Member States on Removal, Grafting and Transplantation of Human Substances*, Resolution (78) 29 and Explanatory Memorandum, 1978.

11 Source: Gallup Survey, USA, 1985.

12 May, W.F. *Religious Justifications for Donating Body Parts*, The Hastings Center Report, February 1985.

13 The Hastings Center: *Ethical, Legal and Policy Issues pertaining to Solid Organ Procurements*, A Report of the Project on Organ Transplantation, 1985.

14 *Organ Transplantation Issues and Recommendations*, Report of the US Task Force on Organ Transplantation, Department of Health and Human Services, Rockville, USA, April 1986, page 28.

15 Childress, J.F. Artificial and Transplanted Organs, *Biolaw* 1986, p. 307.

16 Caplan, A. *Organ Transplantation: The Costs of Success and Organ Procurement: It's not on the Cards*. The Hastings Center Reports of 1983 (December) and 1984 (October).

17 See 14, Report of the US Task Force on Organ Transplantation, from page 96 onward.

18 See 15, Childress.

19 Starzl, Th.E.: *Will Live Organ Donations no longer be Justified?*, The Hastings Center Report.

20 Griffith et al. Temporary Use of the Jarvik-7 Total Artificial Heart before Transplantation, *New England Journal of Medicine*, Vol. **316**: 130–4 (1987).

21 Capron, A.M. *When Well-Meaning Science Goes Too Far*, The Hastings Center Report, February 1985.

22 Source: Gallup Survey, USA, 1985.

23 See 14, *Report of the US Task Force on Organ Transplantation*, pages 43–45.

24 Ibid., pages 102–104.

Organ Transplantation

Report of Discussion Group

A. Van der Werff

We were in the capable hands of Dr Vilardell, our Chairman, and started with two speakers — Dr Westerborn who gave us a report of a survey of public attitudes about organ transplantation in Sweden and Madame Descamps who discussed four case histories from France.

Dr Westerborn described to us a survey on public attitudes with respect to organ transplantation which was highly relevant and had meaningful results for transplant policies in his country. We would recommend that similar surveys on public attitudes with respect to organ transplantation should be carried out in all countries and periodically updated. It would also be advisable to make these surveys internationally so that cross-cultural conclusions could be drawn from them. Maybe WHO or the Council of Europe could coordinate such activities.

Then, from the discussion we found that transplant technology not only favours the transplant itself, but also has broader effects. Transplant technology covers all fields of medicine and through transplant research new knowledge is made available to medicine at large. Many examples can be quoted, such as progress made in immunology. From the discussion with Madame Descamps, we began to debate the problem of living donors. Coercion was seen as a negative point in the ethical equation. In addition, medical objections against the use of organs from living donors were mentioned. For example, kidney transplants seem to cause hypertension later in the life of the donor and Professor Starzl in the United States reported 21 cases of death from living donors. Some members of the working group therefore argued that the use of non-regenerated organs from living donors should be entirely discontinued.

The point was raised, however, that the developing countries cannot do without living donors because they have no life-support systems or other technical facilities to determine brain death. As this is an international forum, we cannot therefore leave out living donors. However, we came to the conclusion that the use of non-regenerative organs from living donors should be restricted to special cases or used for specific medical reasons only, and that such organs should only be donated or removed from legally adult persons of sound mind who have given their full consent in writing on the basis of an independent medical advice.

With respect to minors, the same rule should prevail. Also minors should have to give their approval, and their will should always be respected. Parents and legal representatives should also give consent in writing on the basis of independent medical advice.

We discussed also time of death. Of course, removal can only be effected when death has occurred, and a person is dead when all functions of the brain have been totally and irreversibly lost — in effect, when brain-stem death has occurred. Naturally, determination of death should be made by a physician in accordance with the most recent scientific knowledge and proven experience, and these doctors should not belong to transplant teams.

Then we went on to cadaver-organ donations and we had a long and in-depth debate there — which returned to the discussion all the time. The two systems debated were "informed consent": meaning that one cannot remove the organs without approval of the deceased (or his/her next of kin), and "presumed consent" allowing removal if no objection is made prior to the death of the donor. In the United States generally informed consent is favoured, completed by approved request systems in hospitals, whereas in Europe, in most countries, presumed consent is applied. Sweden and Denmark reported that the development is from presumed consent to informed consent and this trend is very much in line with what doctors want and do. Once more we heard from France that, although presumed consent is allowed by law, doctors do not apply this system, but prefer to ask the family of the deceased for approval. Even in Belgium where recently new legislation was enacted based on presumed consent and a national registry was introduced for those who object, the medical profession has decided not to follow the legal system of presumed consent, but simply ask always and in all cases the family for approval.

However, we decided that both systems should be compared. There are two different solutions based on the same principle. This principle should be that the will of the deceased person, i.e., the donor, should always be respected. We agreed that the will of the deceased is paramount under all circumstances. Appropriate and simple mechanisms should be developed or applied for determining the wishes of the deceased or his/her next of kin. These mechanisms and regulations can vary from country to country.

The group was very strong in its judgement that the sale of organs for profit or payment of any kind to any person for human organs or tissues removed from any living person or any dead body, or part of, should be strictly forbidden. This refers particularly to the developing countries, where they have to rely on living donors.

The next issue on our agenda was organ and tissue procurement. We confirmed that education of the public and professional education are predominant — this means that the burden should not be on the people at the particular moment of bereavement but, instead, that everything should be done prior to that moment to educate the people and to convince professionals. All professionals involved should accept the responsibility for identifying donors and for referring such donors to appropriate organ-procurement organizations. All hospitals should adopt the required request mechanisms for identifying potential organ and tissue donors and for offering next of kin appropriate opportunities for donation. All hospitals should also be affiliated to unified organ-procurement organizations or agencies. We think that this is true of Europe and the United States.

We also discussed supra-national or international organ-procurement organizations and the cost involved, and we recognized that such organizations would be very good sources of statistical information.

Now, we come to costs. There was agreement that everyone who needs a transplant should have equal access to an organ regardless of ability to pay. This means also that the cost of transplantation should be covered by public funds. Such a recommendation would be applicable in both Europe and the U.S.A.

We discussed also the problem of the ethics of general cost containment and what criteria and priorities should be set. Moreover, we debated the indicators that would be needed to compare quality of life versus costs. But one of us said that such indicators could never replace the perceived benefit of one individual's life. If there is a shortage, then one has to decide to refrain entirely from transplantation or to introduce a system of rationing. To enable rational decisions to be made, criteria should be published so that at the micro-level patients can be selected on the basis of criteria that are publicly stated and defended. Decisions at the macro-level with respect to priorities and the allocation of costs, should also be based on criteria that are publicly stated and defended. Finally, the observation was made that in periods of scarcity the required resources for life-saving or life-enhancing treatment should be allocated without restricting development in other, equally important areas of medicine and health care.

The last point of the agenda of the working group was transplant legislation. In some countries current legislation seems to be out of date or non-existent. Moreover, differences exist between countries. For these reasons the recommendation was made that governments should enact comprehensive transplant legislation and collaborate in a joint effort of harmonization.

Health Care of the Elderly — Ethical Issues

D. Callahan*

One of the important demographic characteristics of developed societies is a rapidly and constantly growing number and proportion of the elderly, in particular the age-group 85 years and over, which is the fastest growing group. There is, at the same time, a diminishing proportion of the young. So far as we can see, this situation is likely to continue for at least some decades. In addition to a changing ratio of old to young, one consequence has been a growing burden of chronic illness. A great irony of contemporary high-technology medicine is its capacity to rescue people, to keep them alive, but not necessarily to leave them in good health. At the same time, it is no less true that, as life-spans are gradually extended, the proportion of elderly who are in good health remains very high as well. So, we have at the same time a very large number of elderly who are in good health and a significant number who are chronically ill.

In these circumstances, the question of allocation of resources to the elderly and the just care of the elderly poses as difficult a problem as we are likely to encounter in biomedical ethics, and for one very simple reason: aging represents the new and endless frontier of biomedical research and health care delivery. It is a new frontier because we have learned, over the past few decades, that it is no longer easily possible to distinguish between those conditions that seem to be inherently connected with old age and those that seem only accidentally connected with it. Increasingly, it is possible to treat conditions of the old which were once thought impossible to treat successfully. Organ transplantation is an example. Old age is also an endless frontier for biomedical research, because it is not likely that we are going to conquer death or overcome the limitations of the body. There will thus always be work for medicine to do on this frontier — and always a need of large, even limitless, amounts of money that could be spent.

Biomedical research and health care delivery have done remarkably well in lowering infant mortality rates. They could be even lower in every country, but not much. Also, most people survive into old age; over 70% now die beyond the age of 65. Inevitably, in the future, concern about the burden of illness or the threat of death will relate, primarily, to diseases that affect the elderly.

The ethical problems related to the care of the elderly can be understood at three levels, of which I shall deal with only two. The first level, which Sir Douglas Black will deal with more explicitly, might be understood as the level of individual clinical care of the elderly: what do individual old people need in order to live as healthy a life as possible? Which among their particular conditions are amenable to biomedical

---

* Director, The Hastings Center, Briarcliff Manor, New York, U.S.A.

research and might need better health care delivery? What is the relationship between the health of the elderly and their economic and social conditions? What ought to be the relationship of physicians with other health care workers in treating the elderly? One can, in other words, come up with a very long list of questions and needs at the individual or the clinical level.

A second level, and the one which will be more my focus of interest, is that of health policy. We see in all countries a constant rise in the amount and proportion of money spent on the elderly. This is an obvious consequence of the increase in their numbers and proportion in the population. However, it raises the question: what is a fair allocation of resources to the elderly? What do the elderly deserve? What ought they as a group to have? How do we balance the needs of the elderly against other social needs?

In trying to unravel these problems, one way to begin may be to ask a fundamental question: what are our social obligations to the elderly? Or, put another way, what do we collectively owe one another as we grow old? Or, put still another way, what ought to be the responsibility of the government — our elected and appointed representatives — in providing basic biomedical research to deal with the conditions of the elderly, and including in health care those techniques and treatments that are already available? One can ask, moreover, what is the source of the social obligation to the elderly?

One common view is that we owe the elderly good health care simply out of respect for their age, for the fact that they have survived, for the fact that they have made earlier contributions to society. Some would talk about a reciprocity theory: that each generation has to take care of other generations in order that all will be taken care of adequately. But even if we agree with such views one can ask: what is an appopriate balance between the provision of acute health care — life-saving care — and the provision of long-term care or the care of the chronically ill? How do we make distinctions among types of care for the elderly in this respect? One can also ask: since the cost of care of the elderly is so very high, how do we balance health care of the elderly against other societal needs? If the elderly are valuable members of our society, how important relatively are their needs, and in relation to what other possible ways of allocating resources? Unfortunately, respect for the elderly, even piety towards them in a classical sense, does not give us answers to such questions.

One issue that has arisen prominently of late in the United States is sometimes labelled "intergenerational equity." How do we decide between the needs of the young and the old? In the United States we are now spending a significantly larger amount of government money on the elderly than on the young. The ratio is approximately 6:1, that is to say, six times as much federal money is going to the elderly, defined as those over 65, as to those under the age of 18. The question has been raised: is this a fair or rational way of allocating resources?

There are many — and here I speak more for the United States than for Europe — who would deny that there is an allocation issue at all. They view the whole discussion of the possibility of rationing and limiting care to the elderly as in itself a kind of social menace. They argue that it is indeed true that we spend a large amount of money on the elderly, but that a great deal of money is wasted and inefficiently used. If we spent our money more wisely there would be sufficient for the young and the old, and hence there would be no issue. Therefore the problem as described is one, not of resources going disproportionately to the elderly, but, rather, of inefficient health care.

Others say that we ought to be "age-blind" in the allocation of resources, that we should look at medical need only. They point to the fact that the elderly are a very heterogeneous group, and that it is impossible to generalize about them as an age-group or to make predictions about the individual aged. By no means, they say, are all elderly sick, or senile, or feeble, or dependent on others, and so on. They argue therefore that in this area, as in any other area, we should simply be "blind" to age just as we should not take account of religion, colour or other characteristics. We should simply ask: what are the medical needs of individual old people?

A third approach which is taken, or at least frequently brought up as a possibility, is that if we were to allow the aged greater freedom concerning the termination of treatment, we could save a considerable amount of money. Indeed, many argue strongly that society ought to allow active euthanasia because many elderly people are kept alive much longer than they want to be kept alive. A more widespread acceptance of euthanasia would be a way of dealing with the problem of the heavy use of health resources by the elderly.

I shall not respond to all of these possible ways of essentially defusing or, in the end, denying that there is a real allocation issue. My own view is that there *is* a real issue, and that a more efficient medicine, or active euthanasia, or an attempt to redefine the issue as one simply of medical needs is not going to be adequate to deal with the task of equitably allocating resources to the elderly in the years ahead. My own belief is that we are going to have to find a way to set limits.

"Medical" need as a way of setting limits simply will not work. Medical need has about it a wonderful ring of scientific objectivity, but seems to me very much a function of the state of available technology. Dr. Thomas Stauzl in Pittsburgh in 1986 did a liver transplant on a 76-year-old patient. This patient surely needed a liver. When that liver fails, as it well may within the next five or ten years, he is going to "need" another liver. If the liver is available and the technology makes it possible to do transplants in 80- or 85-year-olds, the "need" will still be there. A person dying of congestive heart disease at 100, or of some other heart ailment, "needs" a heart transplant or "needs" an artificial heart. Once we have an artificial heart that can be implanted in the elderly, the "need" will exist. "Need" is technology-dependent and cannot be defined independently of technology.

I believe, then, that we are going to be forced, in some sense, to use age as a standard; and here one sees some differences between Europeans and North Americans. In the United States we are extraordinarily reluctant to use age as a standard for the termination of medical treatment. We have carried out a campaign for the past two or three decades against discrimination against the elderly as useless and burdensome. This campaign — which has been labelled "anti-age-ism" — has been very successful. We try, as far as possible, to disregard age as a feature of people and hence there is enormous resistance if one utters the notion that age be consciously, clearly and openly used as a standard for the allocation of resources — this is one of the great heresies in American medicine.

This kind of resistance does not seem nearly so strong in Europe. So far as I can make out, in Europe age is used as a standard for limiting and terminating treatment but used tacitly and more by informal than by formal mechanisms. There have not been public debates in European countries about the use of age as a standard, but it does seem to be accepted. Moreover, there seem to be some interesting cultural differences as well. Europeans seem to be more willing to accept death than are Americans, and more willing to understand that medicine may have some limitations.

If we are going to deal adequately with the question of allocation of resources to the elderly, we are going to have to come down to some fundamental questions, of a kind that is rarely asked. One such question is: what ought to be the proper goals of medicine in caring for the elderly? The question of the proper goals of medicine is one that is not much discussed. We take it for granted that we already *know* what they are, namely, the conquest of illness and disease and the relief of suffering. The question is, however, on the edge of the endless medical frontier that is old age: can health care of the aged simply be defined conventionally or are we going to have to ask whether there are possible limits to the goals of medicine? If there are such limits, ought they perhaps to be faced and grappled with more directly in the case of the aged? Is it a *de facto* goal of medicine to relieve all human disease so far as people wish to have disease relieved? We do not ask many questions about the nature of suffering. We also seem to have a *de facto* goal of acquiring indefinite life. No one in medical research will openly claim that medicine seeks bodily immortality. Nonetheless, medicine always wants a little more of life and it still resists seeing people die of possibly curable diseases. The question is: are we going to have to rethink this entire situation?

A related question, no less important, is how we ought now to think about aging as a human phenomenon, given the possibility that medicine will be able to deal successfully with many of the conditions that we associate with old age, particularly many of the debilitating and legal conditions. Are we perhaps open to redefining old age? In the United States there are some who have redefined old age. There is a wonderful saying that "old age is the beginning of a new life", instead of treating it simply as the last phase of life. One might concede it is the last phase, but that it can be a very long, a very happy and a very productive phase.

134

Given medicine's potential for constant progress and for promoting a steady increase in average life expectancy, how ought we now to think about aging? What is old age in an era of medical advance? What is medicine in an age of, on the one hand, the possibility of a greater extension of the human life-span and yet, on the other, a shortage of resources to take advantage of all the things which might be done?

I would argue that we will have to come up with a theory of limits by trying to think through what people ultimately need — not what their organs need, but what they as persons need to live an adequately decent, long life. What do we want to count as an "adequately" long life? The goals of medicine, I believe, ought to be the avoidance of premature death (but now we have to redefine what we mean by premature death); getting people though a decently long life-span (we must also ask what we mean by this); and, finally, the relief of pain and suffering.

It is the definition and meaning of these goals — and note that I omit, quite deliberately — the extension of individual life for its own sake — that must preoccupy us if we are seriously to grapple with the issue of devising fair and just allocations to the elderly. We cannot possibly attempt to do everything medically feasible for the elderly in the years ahead. We must reopen the discussion of just what, within some framework of limits, the elderly most need in order to live lives of honour and dignity, and to die humane deaths.

Health Care of the Elderly — Quality of Life and Aging

Sir Douglas Black*

Issues in care of the elderly

In developed countries, improvements in social conditions and advances in medical knowledge have had important consequences for the care of the elderly in society. Largely because of improved conditions, but also because of better preventive and curative medicine, more people are living not merely to pensionable age, but to ages at which increased dependence is to be expected; at the same time, the number of actual or potential contributors to the resources of society may be diminishing, as a result of measures to control the increase of population. These two factors together raise an economic problem, which has of course also an ethical dimension. There is the further ethical problem raised by the many, often costly, ways, in which life can be prolonged, but the quality of life may not be satisfactory either to the elderly person or to relatives.

These general views raise a number of specific problems, which may be put in the form of questions:

(1) What relative priority should be given to the care of children, of the working population, and of the elderly?

(2) What is the relative contribution of doctors, of nurses and of 'carers' in the community to the care of the elderly?

(3) What is the appropriate training for doctors with a substantial responsibility for the medical care of the elderly?

(4) What is an appropriate balance between care of the elderly in institutions and care in the community?

(5) Are there circumstances in which life may be terminated? Must it always be prolonged by 'unnatural means'?

It is obvious from the nature of these questions that although there is a professional medical contribution to be made to the answers, and also a personal one, the ultimate answers are to be determined by society. Within the framework of that recognition, I give a personal opinion on each of them.

(1) Priority of resources From a purely economic standpoint, the health of productive workers should perhaps be the first priority, but luckily in a developed country they do not place a major burden of illness on the health services. The real dilemma is between children, including the maternity services, and the elderly, both of which categories make very heavy demands. The ideal answer would be 'both'; but I have to confess that if a choice is necessary at the margin I would have to award the higher priority to the care of mothers and children, which is where the future lies. I have heard it argued that the elderly, having paid taxes all their lives, should have the highest priority, but I don't believe it!

---

* Past President, Royal College of Physicians, London.

(2) Doctors, nurses and 'carers' Although doctors may have a critical role in crisis intervention, the long-term care of the elderly lies with nurses, with health visitors and home-helps, and above all with relatives.

(3) Training of doctors All doctors should have training in the special problems of the elderly, given by teachers who have particularly dedicated themselves to the care of the elderly, viz., specialist geriatricians, who should be available in each medical school. However, a great deal of the actual care of the elderly is given by general practitioners and by general physicians and surgeons in district hospitals. I share the view of the Royal College of Physicians of London that there is a role both for 'pure geriatricians' in the major centres and for 'general physicians with a special interest in the care of the elderly', and appropriate training both in general medicine and in geriatrics.

(4) Institution or community This is another of those questions which appear to be 'either/or', but to which the answer is really 'both', depending on the particular circumstances of the case. There is a pragmatic answer, of course, in the complete inability of the public sector to cope with further increase in numbers in long-term care. This has led in the UK to a considerable development of private long-stay institutions, perhaps of uneven standard, though theoretically open to inspection. The 'conventional wisdom' reads 'as much as possible in the community'; but this may represent an apparent economy of visible funding, at the expense of an unquantifiable social cost to relatives.

(5) 'Euthanasia' and 'unnatural prolongation' To be blunt about it, I believe active euthanasia to be incompatible with both Judaeo-Christian morality and medical professional ethics. On the other hand, it is not necessary to give complicated and exacting treatments in every case of life-threatening illness where the outcome is likely to be 'a living death'. It is important, however, that rational patients should be the ultimate judges of the quality of their possible lives, and not doctors or relatives, who may have 'had enough' of their chronic illness.

General Principles

Now, I thought what I would do would be to put out a number of recommendations or principles, and I emphasize that these are, so to say, all my own work — they have not been subjected to the scrutiny of the working group, though I hope that we may be able to do that this afternoon.

1. The Elderly are Entitled to Care and Protection

The first principle that I would suggest is that both by virtue of natural justice, whatever that is, and in recognition of their previous contributions to society and those contributions which they are still capable of giving, elderly men and women have the same entitlement as all other citizens to the care of their family and to the protection of society. This seems to me to be a general principle which ought not to arouse any particular problems so long as one remains with it as a matter of theory. When you start thinking of how to put it into practice, of course, then difficulties naturally begin to appear.

2. The Elderly do not Constitute a Single Class, Group or Category

Then the second thing really arises out of the discussion in the working group yesterday and we were led towards it by Dr Jonsen, who asked the very pertinent question: "Does it make any sense at all to be thinking of 'the elderly' as a single class?" and we very soon agreed that there is no such thing as 'the elderly' taken as a class: even if groups of elderly may have to be considered for societal purposes. Elderly people really have to be considered as individual men and women, and trying to put this perception into the form of some kind of recommendation — I thought that something like this might perhaps do: The obligations of the family and of society can best be discharged if there is a clear recognition that 'the elderly' do not constitute a single class, group or category. In their totality they are as varied as any other grouping of human beings such as children, farmers, or Social Class III in our Registrar-General's classification. In other words, it is perhaps convenient to think of a whole class of elderly people but again when one gets down to practicalities one has certainly to subdivide the problem and, I would say, actually individualize it. Elderly people are all individuals and it is very important not only to recognize this but also to ensure that, whatever measures of care one applies to the problems of the elderly, the important thing is not to do anything which will threaten the individuality of a particular person with whom one is concerned.

I should like at this point to raise the tone of this presentation by quoting from the visionary poet, Blake, who said: "He who would do good to another must do it in minute particulars" in other words — individualize it. "General good is the plea of the scoundrel, the hypocrite, and the flatterer" — people who talk in wide general terms often manage by doing so to obscure the particular, which is where individual actions at least can be most productive.

Well, these seem to me to be two general principles. Both family and society have a real duty to elderly people and elderly people must be treated as individuals and, whatever care is given to them, it must be individualized. I would emphasize, I think, that the rights of the elderly are equally matched by rights of other members of the community. One does not want to get into a situation where one is setting off elderly people against children, or against the working population, because these people also have got their societal rights and it is a very difficult task for the policy-maker and for the allocator of resources to come to a fair balance between competing groups and competing individuals. It is a very serious and difficult responsibility, and I thought that the outline of it which Dr Callahan gave us yesterday excellently fulfilled that particular part of the function which was laid upon us.

3. Recognizing the Individuality of Old People

Now there are a few other things to which I would draw your attention, not perhaps of that breadth of generality, but nevertheless I think important. The third principle I would put forward is this — that recognition of the individuality of old people is an important prerequisite for the proper satisfaction of their needs. Such recognition is most likely to be achieved within their own family or within a small community, not that these are always possible but they represent some kind of ideal. One aspect of individuality which requires attention is the very different wishes and expectations of elderly people themselves. These should be taken fully into account after having been elicited by careful enquiry. You can see that there are very different societal perceptions by elderly people themselves of what the right way is to help with their problems. I shall elaborate this point a little by saying that in many societies these obligations are clearly recognized and fulfilled within the family setting, and this is good, possibly ideal. Nevertheless, this ideal — as I have called it — is threatened by the replacement of the extended family by the nuclear family — this is one consideration. The increased dispersal of family members — it may even be to different countries — is a second consideration. And there is a third consideration, the increasing ratio in many societies, including most of those represented here, of elderly people in need of help to the workers who form or provide the economic base of society. These are all, I think, rather simple and obvious things but nevertheless it is important to state them rather clearly.

4. Balancing Health Technology with Family Care and Social Services

I think it is not very clearly recognized that in the overall care of elderly people medicine and even nursing have a relatively small part to play in comparison with the family, and with other social services even. Nevertheless, medical advances constitute an important part of the problem because, on the one hand, they are contributing both to the prolongation of life, which is in a way part of the problem, and even more vitally to the diminution or lessening of disability (this is even more important in my view than prolongation of life). But, on the other hand, these same advances also bring economic problems through their intrinsic cost, because some of the medical advances are extremely costly. This does not, I may say, apply to all medical advances; if one looks at the global cost of health services it is not as often due largely to high technology; it is due rather to the accumulation of perhaps some unnecessary items of rather low technology. In other words, sloppy medicine is a much more wasteful thing than high technology, and in particular sloppy medicine that consists in doing investigations not because they are needed to influence diagnosis and treatment but just in case someone in a court happens to ask for them. This is no doubt irrelevant, but I happen to find it interesting.

5. Matching Degrees of Dependency with Availability of Facilities and Support

By virtue of their increasing numbers and also the high dependency of a minority of elderly people, their care does constitute an increasing burden on society, and this has to be considered in relation to other calls on resources. In other words, given that medical needs are infinitely expansive and that resources sometimes seem infinitely limited, there are going to come a succession of quite difficult choices. These arise again both at the macro-level (how much is it reasonable for society to devote to the care of elderly people as opposed to other competing demands?) and, very importantly, at the micro level, in deciding what types of provision are best adapted to the needs of particular elderly people themselves.

In the sad tale of growing older and older man moves from health to something called "non-health". It is in reality a process of increasing dependency and it is inappropriate to provide facilities which are more complex than the degree of dependency demands. This is one danger, because by doing it, by providing too much in a way, you can actually trespass on inherent independence. For example, if people who could perfectly well be looked after by their families, or even be in a completely independent situation within the community, are institutionalized, it immediately threatens their independence and pushes them further along the road towards "non-health" than they might necessarily be going at that particular time.

It is a very fortunate that only a minority of people need the more sophisticated and more expensive degrees of institutional, or medical, or nursing care. The great majority of people can be looked after by community care, which has different degrees of care, from just facilitating care — where you help people, as it were, to help themselves — right up to extremes of primary medical care with almost total dependence on nursing care. This is a useful formulation of the relationship between degrees of dependency and what constitutes appropriate care; and, of course, like many other medical things, it does have an economic and also an ethical and a societal dimension. To overprovide can be as destructive of character as to underprovide, and the trick, as it were, is to get a good match between the degree of dependency and the availability of facilities.

Those elderly people who cannot be cared for within the family require a range of medical, nursing and social services which will provide care at a level appropriate to their degree of dependency. This, in a way, is a summary of what I have just been saying rather more diffusely.

Some kind of care is needed to prevent any sapping of independence arising from the type of provision. For example, care within the community when possible is preferable to institutional care, but one must immediately correct this by saying that when this is no longer

141

possible then institutional care is vitally necessary. Thus progressive dependency has to be matched by increasing support, but the degree of support should not be such as serves to increase dependency.

6. Preventing Discrimination Against the Elderly

Now there was a very important point which was brought up again in our working group. When I was presenting the report to the working group yesterday afternoon, I paid tribute to our two panellists and I have already mentioned Professor Jonsen and his insight into the stupidity, as it were, of lumping all the elderly and their needs together. I should now like to pay a similar tribute to Dr Roscam Abbing, because he it was who pointed out to us the vulnerability of elderly people in society and the extent to which they might be exploited by unscrupulous agencies, as in progressive loading of insurance premiums, for example. There is a great tendency for the intermediary providers and the financers of health care to regard the elderly as a vulnerable group and it is particularly important that they should not be preferentially loaded against, as it were. I think in the UK (I've been careful not to give too many examples from my own country) provisions that we have, such as exemption of the elderly from prescription charges, present the good side, as it were, of discrimination.

Health Care of the Elderly

Report of Discussion Group

D. Callahan

Our group did not attempt to develop a series of recommendations. We simply tried to understand the nature of the problem and to engage in some classification of issues. My report will reflect that process. I suppose the number of items put before us must have been close to 75 or 100. There was no shortage of issues and clearly — in talking about health care for the elderly — one is dealing with a very broad social problem; it transcends the borders of medicine and health care.

One prominent category of issues was what I would call conceptual problems: how do we want to define terms and how do we want to engage in classification? There are, moreover, conceptual problems that have significant moral and value implications. Thus at one level the question is simply how ought we to classify and understand certain concepts concerning the aged; and yet at another level, the way we go about that process and the conclusions we reach will have significant moral implications.

The first and most fundamental question was whether one can legitimately generalize about the elderly at all. It is possible to come up with accurate generalizations about the elderly that take account of individual differences among the elderly? There were suggestions that the very effort of trying to come up with general statements about the elderly was itself perhaps harmful to the individuality and variety among the elderly. If one is going to classify the elderly as a group — as, say, distinguished from other age groups or other groups in the popula-tion — what are the purposes for which one is going to do that and what differences do those purposes make? How does one avoid stereotyping the elderly? How does one avoid, if one is going to classify, classifications that may be demeaning, that may place the elderly in a false or wrong light? It was obvious that in our group there were conflicting perspectives on the classification. In great part the conflicting perspectives came partly from a scientific concern: can one accurately generalize about the old? But, there was also a moral concern: if one does generalize, does this open the way for some dangerous consequences?

A second conceptual issue was that, if one agrees that perhaps some classification is necessary, how do we want to define "the old" and "the aged" now? Who is to be so classified? What differences do recent biomedical and demographic and other changes make? In many societies 65 has been a standard retirement age, one that dates back to early policies in Germany. Other societies — Japan, for instance — have used earlier ages for retirement. Some countries have now abolished an official retirement age altogether. Distinctions have sometimes been made between the young-old, the old-old, the frail-old, the very old.

Given recent demographic changes do we want to engage in these classifications? We must recognize of course that if we begin making such distinctions that will have some bearing not only on the way society understands the old and decides who is or is not old but also on the self-understanding of the old. The old will understand themselves in great part by virtue of the way society understands them.

A third conceptual issue was that of minimal levels of necessary health care – minimal levels of health care for all age groups but, in particular, minimal levels of health care for the elderly as an age group. Are we able to define "minimal levels"? It was strongly suggested that we certainly ought to try, that it would have a very important bearing on the allocation of resources and the delivery of health care. The question was then raised: What is the relationship between health and aging? It was pointed out strongly by many that the old are as a group not all sick; most are in fact healthy. Some are very sick, some are very needy, but how, in thinking about both the definition of the elderly and the needs of the elderly, are we to relate health needs to the way we classify and understand the elderly?

Is aging a normal process? Of course, in one sense it is normal but given the possibility of biomedical intervention and change, it is possible perhaps to define aging as disease, saying it is open to biomedical intervention much the same as many other conditions are. If we define aging, however, as a normal rather than a disease process, what do we mean by that? If one defines it as normal as distinguished from defining it as a disease, one is then likely to come to different value stances and perspectives as to whether it ought to be fought or whether it ought to be accepted. If one believes that aging is normal — and that aging ought to be accepted — then one might have a different attitude to the allocation of resources than if one understands it to be a disease, an aberration, something not to be accepted.

A question that came up frequently referred to the notion of quality of life — can we define an adequate, decent quality of life for the elderly? What would be the constituents of such a definition? What are the implications of different types of definitions that we might use? Talking about the quality of life leads us directly to the question of how we will define "need" among the elderly. We can talk about "medical need", on the one hand, and "social, welfare, economic need" on the other hand. Those classifications have both moral and political implications.

It was also asked: how are we now to understand the nature of the life cycle, and the different phases and stages of life? One participant pointed out that we now tend to use adulthood as the paradigm. We see children as those who have not reached adulthood and the elderly as those who have passed it. Is this an appropriate paradigm or should we understand the life-cycle in a richer way, not using one particular stage as the pardigm but rather recognizing that each stage has its particular problems and benefits, opportunities and possibilities?

These were some of the conceptual issues with which we dealt.

A second category of issues we discussed I would classify as moral dilemmas; that is, those issues where some important values are pitted against one another. One moral dilemma, initially raised in my own presentation, was whether we need a theory of limits pertaining to health care for the elderly. It is appropriate to talk about limits for the elderly as distinguished from limits of health care for other groups? Does singling out the elderly for discussion of limits itself perhaps raise some difficult questions concerning the way we understand and classify the elderly?

Another obvious moral dilemma is that of proper balance of resources among and between generations. Most specifically, what is the right way to balance resources between the young and the old? Both age groups have obvious claims — there are goods to be served in each case and yet in the actual allocation of resources we can have a very serious dilemma in deciding who deserves what and on what basis.

Another issue is how we are to find a proper balance between home care for the elderly and institutional care. It is clear that under certain circumstances home care would be ordinarily appropriate; under other circumstances institutional care would be appropriate, depending upon the physical state or condition of the older person. Yet that question in turn raises the question of distribution of obligations. How are we to balance off family obligations to take care of the elderly over against governmental obligations? How are we to decide on a burden of care to be placed upon the family that seems an acceptable and reasonable burden of care? Or, one might say, at what point does one exceed the bounds of reasonableness in providing care and at what point ought the government to come in and, if so, in what way?

There are moral dilemmas concerning research allocation. Some research could aim to extend life. Other forms of research could intend primarily to improve the quality of life. Should we spend money on heart disease, which is a killer, or cancer, which is also a killer, or on arthritis or other conditions that are not lethal but obviously cause a great deal of pain and suffering? One can obviously also see a dilemma about resources devoted to acute care versus resources devoted to chronic care.

We touched briefly on the question of euthanasia as a general moral dilemma. Euthanasia is obviously a moral dilemma very broadly for society, but one can ask whether euthanasia represents a special moral dilemma in the care of the aged and in societal stances towards the elderly.

A third category of issues, I would label "moral reforms that are necessary." I call them "moral reforms" because they were not issues where people seemed to be divided in our group, and they do not on the surface seem to create the kind of agonizing hard choices that perhaps one would find in other areas, but nonetheless do represent important moral concerns. One moral reform upon which we all agreed was that there ought to be a more prominent, active participation of the elderly in determining their own fate and welfare. They ought to be better represented in policy decision-making; and it would be helpful towards that end to see the development of advocacy groups for the aging.

Another needed moral reform would be better care for older women. By and large, older women receive poor care and experience poor economic conditions throughout all of our countries. It was also agreed that a most useful reform would be a better integration of medical and other social and welfare services. By and large, they are too separate now. In many situations of care for the aged it is not only difficult to make the distinction between medical and social needs, but even if one can make the distinction the provision of those forms of services ought to be coordinated much better than it is at present. The theme of integration was agreed upon as an important one — integration of the kind just mentioned — but also integration of various agencies working on behalf of the elderly and better integration of the professions and the professional perspectives of those dealing with the elderly.

There is a strong need to create new social roles for the elderly. There is a great deal of uncertainty in all our societies about just what the elderly are supposed to be, to do, and to represent. With extended life expectancies the elderly are much more in our midst and the question is then: How might we redefine or clarify the present roles of the elderly? This of course has important bearings on stereotyping of the elderly and what we see as the possibilities of the elderly. It would be valuable to attempt to strengthen the family. If the family is to be a major source of care of the elderly, then we have to look to the welfare of the family to make certain that it can play this role as well as possible.

There were other issues raised that I will simply mention. We did talk about the need for international exchange. There are important and illuminating differences between what is going on in North America, particularly in the United States, and what is going on in Europe. We talked about the different emphasis in values, noting for instance that the concept of autonomy seems to be one that has migrated from North America to Europe. Europe in turn has sent North America the notion of integrated national health services and health care availability for all. Questions were raised about different standards of health care in different countries, about carrying out medical research on the elderly, and there are clearly different standards about the social role and place of the elderly. There might be some significant value in greater dialogue and exchange of information between Western and Eastern Europe and clearly also between the North and the South.

Finally, there is the question of what are the proper value and ethical priorities in trying to provide health care for the elderly? What are the principal values that we want to promote and once we have decided on those values, how do we rank order them and decide upon appropriate priorities for political action?

I might sum up our discussion by saying that it became very clear in talking about health care for the elderly that we are genuinely entering into a new era. There have been many effective programmes for the elderly in the past, but there have been such radical demographic and medical changes of late that we now are going to be forced to re-think many things. This re-thinking must begin with the way we understand basic concepts and use terms. We are going to have to come up with some new values; we are going to have to not only devise better delivery systems but also engage in a number of experiments over the next few years. It was particularly suggested that it would be valuable to exchange information, much better than we do at present, on the many experiments now going on for the provision of health care for the elderly. It ought to be possible for us to learn from these experiments many valuable things and perhaps in the process to clarify some of the more fundamental value and ethical questions.

Lifestyles and Health Hazards — Individual Choices and Collective Interests

M. Bégin*

In 1974 the then Minister of National Health and Welfare of Canada launched a small book entitled *A New Perspective on the Health of Canadians*. It was a "working document" which pushed Canada to the forefront in the health policy field and which is still quoted in Canada by every reformist element of the health system. It is also quite familiar to other governments and to WHO. Each minister of health in Canada has referred to it in speeches, panels and exchanges of many kinds in the following years, and it is still as current as can be. It is now out of print and those who have a copy cherish it as a Bible of what health orientations should be in this latter part of the twentieth century. The report was in line with a previous one, as famous in its time: the so-called Hastings Report on community health centres, released by the Federal Government in 1972. Yet, generally speaking, the public knows nothing about those documents and their contents. The Canadian health system is still a curative, "high tech", biomedical model, typical of most Western health systems. Health promotion and prevention, as I could witness myself during the seven years that I was one of those ministers of health in Canada, are definitely the poor relatives of the health system. Why is this?

Let us immediately discard a few possible explanations, the first coming to mind being the accessibility of the system. Canada is a country with universal health insurance (financed by general taxation), first introduced at the provincial level through a federal policy mandate and funding agreement. In other words, health is "free" (pre-paid) for anyone residing in Canada and there are no deductibles. Although many initiatives in health care are federal, the delivery of health care is provincial and decentralized. Canada's spending on health puts the country in the middle range of expenditures according to the annual reporting of the OECD. So, if money and accessibility are not obstacles to a re-orientation of the health care system, what are? Is it fair to conclude that there has been a complete failure of health policymakers in regard to health promotion and disease prevention? Why has good logic not worked? Do Canadians (and others for that matter) still have poor lifestyles which include expensive self-imposed health risks? How could change be engineered and implemented? How far can governments go? Is legislation an agent of social change or merely a reflection of reality? Has a new value system developed, displacing society's cohesion, and in what direction is it aiming? What is the ethical dimension of such common, high-risk behaviour?

---

* Women's Studies, University of Ottawa, Ottawa, Ontario, Canada.

Before exploring the topic under discussion, let me clarify the angle from which this presentation evolves, and I quote from Dr. Bankowski's letter: "... the macro-aspects of environment, health hazards and lifestyles". I understand this to imply the self-imposed risks on health, which could be listed as follows:

(1) Drugs: alcohol addiction; social excess of alcohol; cigarette smoking; abuse of pharmaceuticals; addiction to psychotropic drugs.

(2) Diet and exercise: overeating; high fat-intake; high carbohydrate intake; fad diets; lack of exercise; malnutrition; lack of recreation and lack of relief from work and other pressures.

(3) Others: careless driving and failure to wear seat-belts; promiscuity and carelessness.

(4) Environment: poverty; contamination of drinking water; pollution of lakes and rivers; inadequate sewerage (especially on Indian reserves); refusal of fluoridation of drinking water; air pollution; crowding, high-rise living and the dearth of intensive-use recreational facilities in cities; working conditions; social alienation.

This list as extracted from *A New Perspective...* has not aged much, except perhaps in vocabulary. Today, we would speak of "acid rain" and "VDT's screens" as being also serious health hazards. For the sake of this discussion, I shall elaborate on the first three blocks of definitions, the fourth one being clearly outside the personal influence of individuals.

A rapid judgment on today's situation, in Canada, would lead me to state that, generally speaking and although much has still to be done, some action has taken place in the following way. *First*, and despite much public debate in some quarters and much talk about "infringing on personal freedom", legislation — including fines — has been passed as to the compulsory use of car seat-belts. However, paediatricians are not yet satisfied (and rightly so!) when witnessing parents driving newborns out of a maternity ward without any belt whatsoever! By extension of the same concept, helmets for motorcyclists have been regulated and the City of Montreal, for example, is now regulating the use of bicycles ("Walkmans" are prohibited, etc.). *Secondly,* some improvements are apparent in the way some groups of the population feed themselves and exercise. What is now called the "yuppy" generation (the French "B.C.B.G.") is serving as an important private-sector market for the food industry (through dietetic frozen meals of all sorts) and for the leisure industry (sports, health clubs, clothing). In North America at least, market forces succeeded where health ministers and policy-makers failed. If changes in lifestyles occurred, they did so for the wrong reasons! (And without a policy directive.) *Thirdly*, some progress did take place towards a "smoke free" society and, in Canada, the majority of the population is now, for the first time, in the non-smoking group.

Relative progress might have been accomplished in the image of health as inclusive of a healthy lifestyle. Personal responsibility for it is a completely different matter. I would submit that most people do not even make the connection between good lifestyle and one's responsibility in it. I had several opportunities to verify this hypothesis through the courses I gave in three universities recently. Even amongst health workers other than physicians, health workers deeply committed to a re-orientation in health matters (including as much de-medicalization as possible of life), the concept of "self-health" (l' "auto-santé") is received with mixed feelings and with uneasiness. Both adults and young students wonder what it really means and how far it ought to go. As an intellectual background in their own minds stands the powerful and valued biomedical model in which one's health is in the hands of someone else, and where the physician is "in charge". Even in feminist classes discussing "Women and Health", women seem rather ambivalent about "taking over". Nurse practitioners would openly discuss with such groups, passing on basic information, "re-empowering" them. Yet there persists a passivity and a resistance when it comes to personal responsibility for one's good health. How can such alienation be explained?

Let me now address the topic as a sociologist. Citizens live in an era of paradoxes when it comes to the co-existing sets of values promoted by society. To understand behaviours, one must recognize the norms behind them. Without any claim to a systematic development of such conflicting value systems, here are four galaxies within which today's individuals operate:

(1) The "me" society of the 'sixties, originating in the vulgarization of psychiatry and psychology, defends values which could be labelled inward-looking and whose aim is the satisfaction of personal development, self-fulfillment, and the reward of individual needs and desires. It operates within the context of the consumer society, with a refusal to even consider intellectually the possibility of limits to growth. Therefore, it is generally assumed that there are no limits to satisfaction either.

(2) The so-called "counter-culture", on the other hand, brings us back to nature and is best exemplified by the ecological movement. It does not constitute an ethical system in itself, although some oppose the movement to the consumer society. It does reject the manipulation of nature by economic forces and by technological advances. One of its spin-offs has been the holistic orientation — an integrated perspective for interpreting one's own needs and for dealing with the human being.

(3) Absolute faith in progress which, in this century, takes the face of an absolute belief in science and technology as the new name for reason. Space exploration and the world of micro-chips are typical new dogmas, surpassed only by biomedical advances, be they in the field of new reproductive technology or in the genetic revolution. Biogenetics has displaced the frontiers of man's accepted behaviour and, although uncertainty and doubt are becoming the norm, citizens are not questioning the concept of progress.

(4) The mass communication society — a worn-out expression — with its volume of publicity, advertising, bits of information bombarding us, and with the universe of images and appearances. Its erosion of the capacity of intelligence is not much recognized, and we all like to believe that we are well-informed and knowledgeable. At the same time,

151

appearances become more important than the realities of life. This distortion used to apply almost only to women, but it is now general.

These are but a few of the co-existing sets of values observable in our societies. Another sociological comment should be added here, before addressing the question of ethics *per se*. It is true that a general increase in the population income, added to increased time for leisure, has led to better lifestyles. (The province of Québec, for example, is now second only to the Netherlands in the ratio of bicycles to the number of inhabitants. How much they are used is another matter.) But individual behaviour is not based solely on market forces and consumerism. Gratification concerns itself with meeting basic material necessities and then some luxuries, but it also concerns itself with competing for what Fred Hirsch's *Social Limits to Growth* calls "positional goods". These are goods which define social status differences among individuals. Their value lies chiefly in the fact that some possess them and others do not. If we take as an example the fitness fad of the "yuppy" generation, we see that it belongs both to the fourth galaxy of values — the image society — and possibly to the first one — personal development — but it also obeys a rule of sociology: individuals belong to health clubs and do their jogging because it shows their success in society. They have "made it", and this suggests a corresponding behaviour shared by most members of the socio-economic group in question. It has no direct relation to health policies and re-orientation. If the ensuing behaviour is good for health, it is simply an incidental benefit.

Let me make yet another observation on the difficulties for citizens to adhere clearly to a set of rules based on identified and conscious values. The faith in science, and in particular in biomedical sciences, does not prevent a state of uncertainty of science in matters of nutrition or of domestic products (cosmetics or cleaning products, for example). The consumer society constantly receives new messages contradicting the preceding ones as to the safety or the value of one particular food over another, of one special product over another, thus injecting banality into issues of major importance for individual and collective health status. As William Leiss writes in *The Limits to Satisfaction:* " ... the present tendency represents a colossal auto-experiment by individuals, based on a naive faith in the power of science to counteract any deleterious side-effects by means of further innovations and new products."

These are the paradoxes individuals have to cope with, trying to decide what behaviour they are going to adopt, and for what reasons. Policy-makers share the same uncertainties, plus a few of their own. Three such areas of constraints are:

1. The internal logic of the biomedical model itself as a limitation, and perhaps even a negation, of the importance of health promotion, disease prevention, and healthy lifestyles. When physicians forget that medicine is not only a science but also an art, they become interested only in demonstrated causal relationships. Good lifestyles are often considered by medical doctors as belonging to the world of "software" and not very serious. Such practices may not be harmful, but they are games, or in the extreme, quackery. When the President of the Canadian Medical Association, in a public speech, makes fun of good nutrition and a healthy lifestyle, what impact can senior policymakers and politicians have?

Very few individuals radically question the validity of the biomedical, curative model. Many call themselves "reformists", and in all sincerity, but what they would like to see happen is the humanization of the practice of medicine. There are yet others who also speak of reform, but what they really want is to enlarge the biomedical model to encompass what is usually referred to as "alternative or soft medicine". At best, the public wants both conventional, "high tech", medicine, and new, holistic, non-invasive approaches, coupled with a complete change of attitude on the part of physicians, from cold and authoritarian to compassionate and egalitarian. But in all three cases, citizens want the physician at the top of the pyramid of care/cure. One only has to witness the bitter feelings in nurses' associations after failing in their campaigns to redefine roles and territories of competence in relation to physicians, and the absence of any accommodation, to realize that doctors have an immensely successful power-base, which nurses simply do not have. (Every health minister also knows it.)

2. The budget limitations of the recession and the expectations of no-growth or limited-growth economies, hence of reduced public revenues and expenditures. If a ministry of health or a government decides to adopt the route of disease prevention and health promotion, it will do so because experts have convinced senior officials and politicians not only of the intrinsic value of good lifestyles, but also that such an approach "will save money". It may very well reduce the burden on the curative health system in the long run, but in the short term it will require new, additional, budgets. The fact that these budgets are usually relatively small offers no consolation: there is no new money. Policy-makers and politicians alike know very well that there is no way that existing budgets for curative medicine can be reduced, even infinitesimally, to give way to programmes promoting good lifestyles.

I may add here that the concrete translation into projects and programmes of good lifestyles — what is called health promotion and disease prevention — is more often than not vague or confused.

3. The internal logic of political life. In the same manner that the very rules of the game of the biomedical model must be understood from within, the nature of politics must also be explored. Although physicians enjoy the maximum prestige and power when it comes to stating opinions on health matters, health ministers also have a role to perform. It is only normal that they would set out to exercise leadership and imprint changes on the health system towards better lifestyles. In our democracies, elected ministers of health are accountable to the public in a direct way, but they are seldom medical doctors. They need meaningful

153

budgets and they need the support of the medical profession. Other factors also come into play, rarely understood by the reformist elements of the health care system. Politicians must be re-elected — nothing cynical in this — and generally, whatever their political ideologies, they will do what they perceive to be the desires of the public. They will not, and cannot, act if there is no public demand. Of course, they can try to create the demand, and they do so at times with success. In the case of health promotion and prevention of disease, I am not convinced that it is a realistic challenge which politicians can meet. The public's behaviour responds to mysterious cues, and I am not persuaded that it was the television and print advertising by governments against smoking — which I approved — that changed the habit of Canadians in such a drastic way. Some deep motivation came into play at a certain point in time, which triggered a massive change in lifestyle. Campaigns by my former ministry surely reinforced the new patterns and nurtured them. But government action followed societal change, being extremely careful to respect the fragile balance between individual rights on the one side and those on the other. It did not precede change of behaviour, for the new norm would have been inefficient. (An example of government action which probably went "too far" for what the society is ready to support in Canada is the new Federal Bill C-51 against any sponsoring of sport or cultural activities by tobacco companies. Quite a backlash is developing while the Bill is discussed by the House of Commons, definitely with some public support. A Gallup poll released by Radio Canada on May 25, 1987 showed strong public support (61%) for banning all advertising of tobacco products. There are even 34% of the public who believe that the government should ban all *sales* of tobacco products! However, it seems that the same public is not ready to cross the fine line now proposed by the Federal Government.)

Referring back to the social sciences and to my own practical experience, I tried to situate, to locate, the discussion of the ethics of lifestyles. Let me attempt to focus now on the ethical dimension of such desired change of orientation of our health care systems.

Earlier on, I made the point that I observed no connection in the public's mind between the need for healthy lifestyles (for their own sake) and their personal responsibility in the matter. To be fair to the public, it must be repeated here that the notion of personal responsibility is somehow diluted in complex, big governments, characterized by the welfare state and by an extensive social safety net. I do not intend to say that the public is not aware, painfully aware, of the taxes paid for the common good, but it has become difficult to associate costs with outputs. A general "dependency syndrome" often co-exists with an acute sensitivity to unwarranted public spending. The sense that the person, the individual, can play a role is gone. Huge, complex, anonymous systems have taken over. The loss, or at least the erosion, of the feeling of personal responsibility probably generates a passivity in many areas of human activity.

What, then, are the other points of reference of a possible ethical

154

system? Life, the very fact of life being at stake, remained through centuries the corner-stone of ethics in health matters. This belief has been eroded with a much longer life expectancy and medical advances keeping patients artifically alive. Moral issues have increased in the last decade to a point never previously reached by mankind.

Medical associations or policymakers are trying to define new codes of ethics. In an essay by David Roy and Maurice A. M. de Wachter in *Traité d'Anthropologie médicale*, the point is made that any new deontology will have to emerge from within the rationale of the biomedical sciences and the practice of medicine. "*Nous sommes sur le point de reconnaître que la déontologie médicale est une question du jugement clinique, et non pas seulement une spécialisation de la réflexion philosophique, ou une intrusion des humanités en médecine*". (We are on the point of recognizing that medical deontology is a question of clinical judgment, and not only a branch of philosophy, or an intrusion of the humanities into medicine.) What, then, is the key to an ethic of proper lifestyles?

In a general and ill-defined way, the new concept that seems to be gaining momentum in public opinion is one of "quality of life". The phrase, which was rather empty a few years back — more an electoral slogan than anything else — is now invested with an undefined, but shared, general meaning applicable to both collective and individual behaviour. It may be used in reference to malformed fetuses or euthanasia, as well as to procedures surrounding terminal cancers (palliative care units). I would call it a new shared value, possibly the basis of a common ethic of which the elements are still unravelled. Its use is now limited to the traditional curative health care system. Is it also relevant to promoting healthy lifestyles? Maybe.

In Canada, the one collective feeling — I hesitate to label it a solidarity — that has emerged in the last ten years is the sense of the protection that our environment needs. Replanting trees, managing forests, protecting waters from human or industrial pollution, respecting wild life, have all constituted a learned knowledge of the ecological balance. What created this awareness? Was it simply information and education of the public? Although I have no proof, I doubt it — but I am sure it helped. In an analogous way, the anti-nuclear movement, which links into the same collective sense of saving one's milieu, may be shared to an extent by all citizens, but it mobilizes to protest action only a small fraction of the public.

If the biogenetics breakthroughs of these years, by their very dramatic nature, have called for a new code of ethics, the same can not be said of campaigns for better lifestyles. The definition of what constitutes health — "a state of complete physical, mental and social well-being and not merely the absence of disease and infirmity" — is not yet entrenched in our minds, nor are the consequences delineated. The focus of what health means remains centred on the biomedical intervention. I am not sure that the public knows that we have reached – as far as the group is concerned — the limits of good health possible under a curative system which does not open up to preventive measures and health promotion. Changes of lifestyle rest at the periphery as something desirable, not as a powerful motive for action. The terms of the public debate — when and if it ever takes place — are not ethical in nature.

Of course, the fight against smoking or the issue of abuse of alcohol can easily be put in moral terms: the freedoms of some against the freedoms of others. But it is not the moral debate that sorted out collective behaviour. Whatever triggered changes in lifestyles, the fact is that non-smokers' "rights" would have been unthinkable 20 or even 10 years ago. Non-smokers were a minority, almost a sect, living in hiding. The collective "rights" were in the other direction; so was the collective norm; and so were public policies. Financial disincentives (not adopted for health reasons, but because of the need of the state for more revenues) and government publicity campaigns might have played a role. I personally believed that they came after the fact, simply speeding up a process of change *still unknown to us.* Today, non-smokers are the norm and, like many newly converted, they are quite vocal. But where is ethics in all that?

If we consider the changes that did happen towards better lifestyles, we observe the following:
- Over-eating and lack of exercise: change operated by the private sector, who sold it to consumers, based on the notion of social achievement and on images of the good life.
- Smoking: change operated through the development of a new societal consensus.
- Dangerous driving: partial change operated by legislation, apparently ahead of public opinion, but accepted by a majority.
- Abuse of pharmaceuticals: possible change taking place through the women's movement and through action by associations of the elderly. (Both are quite concerned that they are the "privileged victims" of over-prescription of drugs in general, and of tranquillizers in particular.)

No changes on other fronts.

Social change is rarely the linear, rational, path one dreams of developing, nor does it follow the prescriptions of policy documents. Erratic (since we do not understand its dynamics), eclectic, accidental and fragmented, it occurs by a case-by-case approach, in a rather pragmatic way. It does not seem to have a master plan, but only historians will be able to tell.

I have tried to assess realistically the slow pace of social change, showing how little we know about its functioning. If I now turn to an idealistic self, I would offer as an avenue worth exploring the quest for the whole person, so badly needed in our extremely fragmented society. The question is quite simple to ask: can a holistic view of the patient be reconciled with overspecialized modern scientific medicine? Although some of the greatest names in medical research as well as some humble general practitioners do know that medicine, for all its scientific developments, still owes much to art, this is not the view shared by

156

organized medicine. It seems to me that if these views — of art and of science — are antithetic we shall not progress. If medicine continues to teach what is known about the body as a materialistic object, leaving the intricacies of the mind to psychiatry, and if physicians remain at a distance from the emotional life of their patients, how can we ever succeed in making better lifestyles more highly valued?

If better lifestyles were ever to become meaningful to individuals, and therefore to society, it would be because of one's need to re-connect with oneself as an entity, in a search for total well-being. But I cannot envisage science and technology as being displaced to a less important role in the prevalent sets of values of the Western World, even if the price to pay is extreme fragmentation, even atomization, of the individual, generating in turn passivity and infantilization of the patient. But of course, for all we know, we may witness citizens living like split personalities and finding their own way to reconcile conflicting systems in a manner yet to be imagined.

Community and Ethics in Lifestyle Changes*

Edwin B. Fisher**

Dr C. Everett Koop, the United States Surgeon General, was very sorry that he could not attend this conference. For me it is a great pleasure to substitute for Dr Koop, not only because of this important conference but also because of my admiration for Dr Koop, himself. He is showing us in the United States how a community can respond humanely to health problems in its midst. Many of the ideas in this paper were suggested to me through conversations with Dr Koop or through his writings. This is especially the case for those sections which deal with AIDS and for the emphases on a caring community and on rights of the individual, discussed toward the end of the paper.

Community and social affirmation of health promotion will be needed to counter the dangers posed by smoking, AIDS, and other risks this conference addresses. The forces promoting health risks extend throughout our societies. They lie in our economies, our businesses, our public gatherings, our folk-ways, and our personal and family lives. To counter these forces, we must work throughout our societies, as caring and determined communities and as nations united to help all our citizens.

In the rest of this paper, I shall use the word "community" to refer to shared concerns and activities of large groups of people. Community efforts include broad social and national efforts to affirm common goals and work to achieve them. As I shall discuss further, community entails mutual caring and assistance, broad social affirmation of shared goals, and respect for individual rights.

Ethical choices surrounding health and lifestyles strike at the most intimate experiences of our lives — birth, love, parenthood, death. Concurrently, they affect us at the most public and collective borders of our awareness, as government policies, mass changes in cultural values and practices, and, as in the case of AIDS, risks of population-ravaging epidemics. Our need to protect ourselves propels us towards ambitious community attempts to understand and control health risks. On the other hand, our concerns for privacy, individual rights, and personal dignity may cause us to draw back from initiating change at a

---

* Preparation of this paper was supported by National Institutes of Health grants CA 41703 (E. B. Fisher, Jr., Principal Investigator), HL17646 (B. E. Sobel, Principal Investigator), and AM 20579 (W. H. Doughaday, Principal Investigator). C. Everett Koop, Surgeon General of the United States, was extremely generous in helping to plan and in commenting on a preliminary draft of this paper. John Bryant, Ana Coelho, David Freedman, Leonard Green, Robert Kaplan, Anna Krijnen, and Julio Santiago also provided helpful comments on a preliminary version.
** Center for Health Behavior Research, Departments of Psychology and Medicine, Washington University, St. Louis, Missouri, U.S.A.

community level. All of these issues are touched by the most important perspectives we take on our own lives, our spirituality, our connections to each other, and our investment in our own integrity. Finally, while these questions can intrigue us and stimulate great amounts of thought, the clock is ticking and the decisions taken or not taken have enormous consequences for us all.

It is not without misgivings that we see ourselves as a part of a larger group. Autonomy and independence are central to much Western thought about individual identity. We fear both the loss of our individual rights and the control of our choices by the group. Our political systems reflect this fear. Religion, too, reflects concern for individual identity. Christianity has evolved with an increased emphasis on a personal relationship of the individual with the Deity. Western economic systems stress the skill and freedom of the individual, who owes others equal opportunity but not equal reward. These concerns for the individual within the group are reflected by serious ethical questions in community health programmes. To what extent does the group have the right to constrain our choices, to prohibit some choices, to guide us to others? To what extent should we be held responsible for the costs to the group of our own habits, such as smoking? In planning community health policy, how much emphasis should be placed on the community's concern for costs and effects of disease aggregated over all its members? How much emphasis should be placed on the individual's perspective on his or her own risk amidst his or her other values, goals, and interests?

AIDS and the Need for Community Health Promotion

While this paper will focus on the ethical issues which arise out of community efforts to promote health, it will focus also on AIDS. AIDS provides a good example of many of the ethical issues in community approaches to health. Also, it is a problem to which we need to devote attention in these times.

Let us begin with a brief review of the problems of AIDS. Cases of AIDS have now been reported in 110 countries. However, I shall deal largely with the USA. I recognize that AIDS and the problems associated with it are different in different countries.

In June 1981, there were five reported cases in the United States. By the spring of 1987, the number had risen to 32 000, and, in 1987, 23 000 additional cases are expected to be reported. While, in the USA, the disease is still largely confined to homosexual and bisexual men, intravenous drug users and prostitutes, it is increasing among heterosexual men and women, as it had previously become common among heterosexuals in other countries (Koop). Several cases of health workers contracting AIDS through contact with blood have been reported by the Centers for Disease Control of the US Government. The path of entry into these workers' own bloodstreams seems to have been superficial, through open wounds of dermatitis, facial acne, and the like.

160

In addition to other social and demographic factors, race is emerging as a striking correlate of AIDS incidence. Overall, the relative incidence of AIDS among black and Hispanic as compared with white men is 2.6 and 2.5, respectively. For black and Hispanic women, the incidence relative to white women is 12.2 and 8.5. Among men abusing intravenous drugs, the incidence for blacks and Hispanics relative to whites is 21.8 and 20.7 (data from Centers for Disease Control, reported in the *New York Times*, August 2, 1987). These trends probably reflect differential exposure, such as through greater sharing of needles in intravenous drug use or reluctance to use condoms. But they also mirror minority groups' reduced access to health care and reduced access to the educational and financial resources which support healthy lifestyles. Most important, the superposition of such trends on background racism is frightening.

Reactions to AIDS have demonstrated what is a major barrier to many community health efforts, the tendency to see a problem as a characteristic of some subgroup rather than as a threat to all. Such a reaction no doubt provides some sense of security for those who are not members of the target groups. Individuals may also be motivated to see themselves as somehow immune to things which threaten everybody. Also, attributing such problems as AIDS to subgroup characteristics means that people use science and clinical concern as a cover-up for old prejudices. In the case of AIDS in the USA, homosexuals, intravenous drug users, and racial and ethnic minorities are prime targets for this reaction. But the facts indicate that AIDS threatens us all. The cases of health workers infected through contact with blood samples and the projected spread of AIDS among heterosexuals make obvious that none of us is immune. It is clear that AIDS is among *us*, not among *them.* Recognition of this fundamental, shared vulnerability and interest seems to be a principal condition for a community effort.

Now let us review some of the things we must do about AIDS. Effective treatment is still a long way off. The AIDS virus is a complex one. Estimates of the time of availability of an effective vaccine run well into the 1990s or past the turn of the century. Since it cannot now be cured, the best public health measure is to control exposure. To achieve widespread use of condoms and other steps to control exposure requires massive public education. The education should begin in the public schools. The reality of sexual activity among adolescents and teenagers compels our arming these young people with the information they need to protect themselves. Of course, many in the USA oppose teaching in the public schools about safe sex and the use of condoms. They see such education as tantamount to condoning sexual experimentation among schoolchildren. This controversy over health education regarding AIDS is a good example of Professor Gorovitz's argument (1987) that ethical questions are intrinsic to health policy. As he pointed out, this is especially so in the absence of a cultural consensus regarding background moral issues, such as lack of consensus about premarital sex, as it affects policy regarding AIDS in the USA.

161

Adults need to be educated that there may be no absolutely safe sex. The best protection is a long-term, monogamous relationship in which the partners are faithful to each other. Those who are sexually active outside a long-term, monogamous relationship must take responsibility for their risks. Use of condoms in sexual intercourse when it is not *certain* that neither partner has AIDS is the central measure to be encouraged. Those who fall within a high-risk group or have reason to believe they may have been exposed to AIDS need to be tested. If they refuse testing, they need to assume they *have* been exposed and act to protect their partners. Those who are not sure that their partners have not been exposed need to assume that they may have been and take appropriate precautions.

Beyond these immediate efforts to control exposure and educate the public, the extent of future health care for AIDS will be staggering. It will include hospital, hospice, or home care for dying patients, testing and monitoring of cases, expensive drugs to control symptoms or extend life, public education campaigns to encourage reduced exposure, and, we hope before too long, mass vaccination. Insurers are already raising concerns about their ability to support projected costs. A recent survey of the personnel and health coverage policies regarding AIDS of 1 000 US companies yielded responses from only 164 (Boulder, Colorado, *Daily Camera*, May 22, 1987). Among these 164 companies, 163 reported medical plans providing treatment for AIDS and two-thirds reported forbidding discrimination against employees with AIDS. Nevertheless, one wonders about the practices of the 836 companies that did not respond.

AIDS presents enormous challenges to all of us. It is clear that these challenges will not be met by individuals acting alone. We must work as a community to care for and educate one another, encourage necessary habit changes, and treat with active compassion those among us who are struck by AIDS. To mobilize the efforts which AIDS will require, we shall have to recognize that each of us needs the rest of us, that we cannot protect ourselves by avoiding "them," in short, that we *are* a community. We shall also have to keep our community open to all. We must not try to isolate or restrict those who are part of us and whose vigorous cooperation we need.

Because of the nature of the AIDS problems, combating it will require concerted national efforts in all our countries. All of us, professionals, citizens and government leaders, will have to support efforts to control AIDS. We shall have to do this through all of the institutions and organizations in which we participate, our families, our communities, our schools, our workplaces, and our governments. We must work together with compassion and determination to defeat AIDS.

Ethical Issues

As we have seen, individual identity and group solidarity often conflict within community health programmes. This conflict is related to a number of ethical issues, of which we shall focus on three. The first concerns the interests of the group versus the rights of the individual. To what extent or under what circumstances is the group entitled to advance its own interests in ways which limit individual rights? The second issue is whether we view lifestyles as freely chosen and thereby the responsibility of the individual, or as determined by social, economic, cultural or other forces which act *on* the person. If we view the person as responsible for his or her own lifestyle, then we may also hold him or her responsible for such consequences of that lifestyle as the costs of medical care for lifestyle-related diseases. The third issue concerns the ethical implications of how we view health. Do we see it as a matter of diseases and organ systems, or as something that pertains to the actions and interests of the whole person? While these three issues all reflect the tension between the individual and the community, distinguishing among them may help us identify specific ways to deal with them.

Individual and group rights The first ethical issue concerns the rights of the group and of the individual. As pointed out by Begin (1987), the needs and interests of the group are not always those of the individual. When community and individual interests are in opposition, it will be difficult to generate broad social affirmation of community health goals. If they do not feel supported by the community, individuals may refuse to cooperate with its policies. We see this clearly in current discussions of limiting the right to smoke in public and of the right to privacy in testing for the AIDS virus.

Tests results alone will not halt the spread of AIDS. It will require the cooperation of those at special risk. Those at risk may fear severe reprisals if friends, employers, or even family members find out they have AIDS or even have been tested. Thus, we must ensure confidentiality of testing and test results. Failure to treat tests as confidential may keep those at risk from being tested and from cooperating in community efforts against AIDS. More generally, failure to consider the rights of the individual may antagonize those very people upon whose cooperation effective policy implementation depends.

Recent debate in the USA has considered requiring those applying for marriage licences to be tested for AIDS and refusing licences to those who test positive. The restriction of the right to marry must surely figure as a substantial intrusion of the group interest on the interests of two individuals. Even the threat of such intrusion is bound to undermine the willingness of those who may be singled out to cooperate with the rest of us.

Parenthetically, it is worth noting how the proposal to restrict the right to marry also illustrates a general characteristic of the interrelations of health, ethics, and public policy. Ethical issues may emerge from changes in scientific knowledge and changes in health problems. For instance, the current level of validity of tests for AIDS would create very serious problems of false positives, especially in a segment of the population with a low base rate of true positives. Fear of such a deadly disease as

163

AIDS may cause the community prematurely to impose obligations, such as to be tested, before the availability of technology that would make such an obligation more helpful than harmful. Testing among those at low risk is also a poor use of public resources, especially in view of current delays of over a month in testing volunteers in some parts of the USA.

Social versus individual responsibility for lifestyles. The second ethical issue is that of individual versus social responsibility for lifestyles or risk factors. Individual responsibility takes a major place in the way Western culture views the relation between the individual and society. Moreover, we tend to view individual responsibility and individual rights as closely connected. If the individual is accorded the right, say, to drink until he is drunk, he is also held responsible for that choice. This is reflected in the legal system in the USA, a central assumption of which is the responsibility of individuals for those consequences of their behaviour which a "rational" person could anticipate. For instance, incapacity due to drunkenness is not a defence against harm done while drunk. A rational person may anticipate such incapacity as a natural consequence of excessive drinking of alcohol, and consequently is held responsible for such consequences.

In view of the recognized health consequences of lifestyle risks, there is a growing movement to hold individuals responsible for these consequences. Insurance rates for smokers provide one example. Assuming that smokers should pay for the costs of their smoking, many insurance companies already give lower automobile insurance rates to non-smokers. There is now a growing move to alter health insurance rates according to smoking status. For almost two years, the Blue Cross and Blue Shield health insurance companies in the state of Minnesota have been giving a 22% rate reduction to non-smokers. The presumed responsibility of the smoker for the health-care and other costs of smoking is also the reason for some discussion of raising cigarette taxes in the USA. Such taxes might be designated to pay for public health-care costs of diseases related to smoking and for public education to discourage smoking.

Taxing smokers to recover the costs of their habits appears to be based on the assumption that smokers are responsible for these costs. Such presumed responsibility appears, in turn, to be based on the assumption that smokers have freely chosen their habits. Yet, a variety of evidence indicates powerful influences of social, cultural, and economic forces over individual lifestyle choices. If we recognize these influences on individual choice, if we see lifestyle choices as determined rather than freely chosen, can we still accord individuals the right to choose? Is it inherently against the individual's right to choose for society to act to encourage healthy choices? We cannot answer these questions here, but we shall sketch out further some of the background to them and some of their implications.

Is it reasonable to view smoking as a habit that is freely chosen? Let us

164

look at some evidence. The USA spends over $3 billion each year marketing cigarettes. A major reason for this expenditure on the marketing of cigarettes is their profitability relative to other consumer products. For instance, dollar for dollar of one large company's gross sales in 1981, selling cigarettes was four times more profitable than selling food and beverages (Fisher & Rost, 1986). Consider further that this marketing is of a demonstrably addictive substance. Consider also that most adult smokers were launched into their habits and probably addicted while still in their teens, before it was even legal to sell them cigarettes in the USA. Indeed, the very laws which limit sales to minors are based on a presumption that minors are incapable of exercising responsibility for choosing to smoke.

The literature linking smoking cessation to psychological and demographic characteristics also bears on the assumption that smoking is freely chosen. Those most likely to quit on their own or with minimal interventions are those who are generally better off or advantaged (Fisher, 1982). They are physically and psychologically healthier (Friedman *et al.* 1979), have greater skills in self-management and problem-solving (Perri *et al.*, 1977), and have greater income (Blair *et al.*, 1980). In the USA, smoking is more prevalent among blacks than among whites (DHSS, 1987) and among blue-collar workers than among white-collar workers (Koop, 1986). This effect of social, cultural, and economic factors on such a habit as smoking should make us question what we mean by so-called "voluntary risks" (e.g., Knowles, 1977).

When we try to explain behaviour which is determined by a wide range of causes rather than by a single, necessary and sufficient cause, we tend to attribute the behaviour to the free will of the person rather than to the many influences acting on the person. Explanations of smoking provide good examples of this tendency. Because factors ranging from advertising campaigns to poverty to racism to peer pressure to addiction contribute to it, we are inclined to attribute smoking to the choice or free will of the smoker rather than to the many influences which bring it about. Among others, B. F. Skinner has discussed these issues in discussing the differences between what we commonly view as voluntary and involuntary behaviour. In general, we categorize as involuntary those behaviours for which we can find an apparent cause which seems to determine with certainty the occurrence of the behaviour. Behaviours we view as voluntary, on the other hand, may have a variety of causes, none of which is especially salient or obviously decisive. Without one clear, decisive cause, we attribute the behaviour to the will of the person and term it "voluntary." As Skinner puts it, though, "The distinction between [so called] voluntary and involuntary behavior is a matter of the *kind* of control" (1965, p. 112) the environment exerts over behaviour, *not* a matter of the *presence* or *absence* of control over behaviour. While the control of smoking by diverse social, economic, addictive, and cultural processes may not be the same as the control of a simple reflex by an unconditioned stimulus, it is still control.

If we now view so-called "voluntary" risks as being determined by diverse social, economic, personal, and biological forces, we must question policies which are based on the assumption that such risks are freely chosen. This need not deter us from measures to *encourage* healthy lifestyles. But we need to examine the ethics of policies which may punish our fellows unfairly for habits or risks caused by diverse forces which they do not control. Especially, if we seek to promote broad social consensus to face serious health threats, we cannot emphasize blame and punishment. We must place as much emphasis on encouraging desirable habits as on discouraging their undesirable counterparts.

It is difficult to identify what constitutes placing as much emphasis on encouraging desirable as on discouraging undesirable habits. A useful principle for guiding our actions in these areas may be that we should act to expand the choices which are *available* to the person. This entails several things. First, we should generally centre our activities and policies on incentives for desirable habits or lifestyles rather than on disincentives or punishments for undesirable behaviours. Second, we should determine whether desirable habits are truly available to those whom we hope to help. We may think of availability as secured by the absence of any active opposition to a person pursuing a particular goal or change. But availability should include not only the lack of obstacles but also the *effective* means to *pursue* a choice or goal. A smoker who lacks the skills to quit smoking cannot be said to have non-smoking as an available choice.

Availability also needs to include the absence of forces which undermine individual efforts. Such undermining forces may not obviously block availability of a desired behaviour but may be very powerful, nevertheless. For instance, there are many in our culture who are politically free to choose not to smoke, to eat a healthy diet, or to exercise regularly but who are inhibited from doing so by stressors and limitations arising from poverty, inadequate education or racism. Amidst such stressors and limitations, the availability of healthy lifestyles is severely compromised.

An example of cultural limitations on the choice of a healthy lifestyle is the impact of cigarette advertising on the choice of quitting smoking. Consider the smoker who is not skilled in evaluating claims and arguments, who may assume that "the government wouldn't let them advertise cigarettes if they were *really* dangerous." For such a person, the availability of a choice to decide to quit or to resist the urge to relapse is compromised. It is compromised by advertising in otherwise credible magazines, which shows attractive, successful, apparently healthy models enjoying cigarettes in situations linked to many of life's satisfactions, such as achievement, popularity, sexuality, and even vigorous physical exercise. The $3 billion spent on marketing and advertising cigarettes each year in the USA reduces the availability of nonsmoking as a choice. This is more money than is spent marketing any other consumer product in the USA. Surely, we must question the values of a culture which allocates such communication and economic resources to *promoting* the largest single cause of avoidable mortality in

166

our country. In such a culture, banning advertising of cigarettes would increase the extent to which the choice of non-smoking is truly available.

Consideration of the resources devoted to advertising and promoting cigarettes in the USA raises interesting questions about freedom and availability of choice. Unless they emigrate, US citizens have no choice but to live in a culture which devotes such resources to encouraging them to smoke. The availability of the choice of quitting one of the most deadly habits in our culture is compromised by $3 billion spent to keep smokers smoking. Surely such influences are substantial infringements on the freedom of citizens. Freedom and free speech in particular are central political values in the USA. But we may question whether freedom is served by interpreting massive advertising of deadly products as free speech.

The present view of availability of choice shares the deterministic perspective of the position set out above that smoking and other lifestyle risks are involuntary, determined by social and economic forces. As smoking is determined by forces outside the individual's control, so the possibility of quitting requires the learning of the skills needed to understand the risks of smoking and to marshall the resources to give it up.

As we have questioned the individual's responsibility for lifestyle choices, we need to affirm the responsibility of the group in community health promotion. Most of our societies have long embraced an ethos according to which the group takes care of its members who need help. If individuals adopt misguided habits, it is the responsibility of society to help them. However, society will fail to reach those it seeks to help if it combines the offer of help with too great an emphasis on individual responsibility for risky choices, through excessive, punitive, or regressive fines, taxes, and the like.

Looking at disease and looking at people. The third ethical issue I wish to discuss is the perspective from which we view health and disease. We have a choice here. We may approach health and health promotion from the perspective of the person as an integrated set of actions, interests, and values, or we may think of health in terms of distinct diseases or organ systems. Madame Begin (1987) put the distinction strongly. She suggested to the Conference that a new ethical code of behaviour lay in the quest for the whole person and the eventual rejection of the extreme fragmentation of the human being, generally, and of the body especially. She views such a holistic approach as incompatible with reductionistic, conventional scientific approaches to the body as an object.

Science tends to investigate things in isolation from their contexts. It tends to look at the force of gravity in a vacuum or the function of an organ independent of the functions of other organs with which, *in vivo*, it interacts. For instance, science may identify the risk of heart disease attributable to high cholesterol, but it cannot evaluate this risk against, say, the aesthetic value of foods that lead to high cholesterol. Thus, it may not be possible to reconcile the perspective of science, quantifying the risk associated with a specific habit, with the perspective of individuals, judging the risk associated with a specific habit *within the context* of all their other habits, values, and aspirations.

Whether the scientific or objective perspective may be reconciled with the personal or subjective is beyond the scope of this paper. Nevertheless, in mobilizing the support of individuals to community initiatives, it is important to think of health as an expression of the person's integrated set of actions, interests, and values, rather than a matter of distinct diseases and organ systems. For a programme to enlist broad support of many individuals, they must see it as making sense according to what is important to their lives, not just according to what is important to the collectivity.

The importance of taking the perspective of the whole person is heightened by consideration of the kind of behaviour required in a community approach to a health problem. By their very nature, for instance, sexual practices related to the spread of AIDS are remote from public scrutiny or public control. Rather, safe sexual practices require individuals to apply and adapt several general principles to their own circumstances and to changes in these circumstances. Regulations cannot anticipate all the instances to which the principles need to be applied nor can public scrutiny be brought to bear on sexual practices in order to monitor and enforce such regulations. Active cooperation of the community is required. Such cooperation is unlikely if policies are imposed on people without reflecting their goals and interests. Active cooperation is enhanced by involving members of the community in setting goals which reflect their views of their own lives and those things which are important to them.

Taking into account the aggregated interests of individuals may be especially helpful in setting priorities among the confusing array of risks and benefits revealed by health sciences. For instance, many in Western societies may feel bewildered by frequent news reports about yet another health risk to avoid. However, placing the latest risk within the context of other health risks and their relative riskiness, weighing it within the context of other things about which the person cares, and recognizing that choices must be made, that life is to be *lived*, may reduce such bewilderment. One who truly enjoys fried hamburgers may sensibly conclude that indulging this habit is trivial relative to indulging the enjoyment of smoking cigarettes.

Considering the aggregated interests of the person is also necessary for setting priorities in the context of limited social and economic resources. For instance, the cost of extraordinary care to preserve life among the terminally ill presents insurmountable ethical difficulties if biological life, itself, is appraised apart from those interests and potentials which give it value. However, if we consider extending life within the context of the entire range of interests and activities which have given an individual's life its meaning and value, we are likely to recognize imperatives which supersede mere duration of survival.

Viewing health risks from the perspective of the person may sound simple, but may require greater changes in how professionals view health than we might at first imagine. Consider the following example in the area of diabetes. A current clinical trial in the USA is exploring the effects of normoglycaemia on vascular complications, as indexed in this trial by diabetic retinopathy. An intensive-treatment protocol designed to achieve normoglycaemia includes (a) self-monitoring of blood glucose at least four times daily, and, *either* (b) injections of insulin at least three times daily, or (c) continuous subcutaneous insulin infusion. A standard treatment has been designed according to a survey of clinical practices among medical centres participating in the trial and includes one or two insulin injections a day and self-monitoring of blood glucose only as necessary to maintain clinical well-being. Those directing the study have based sample-size calculations and other design features on the expectation that achieving normoglycaemia will reduce the rates of retinopathy by 30%.

Results of a 12-month feasibility phase of the trial indicate that the intensive treatment led to appreciable and sustained increases in glycaemic control (The DCCT Research Group, 1986, 1987). If subsequent phases of the study confirm the reductions in retinopathy expected through intensive treatment, then the public health implications would appear clear: those with diabetes should be helped and encouraged to maintain blood glucose as close to normoglycaemic levels as possible.

Further results of the feasibility study, however, raise questions about the desirability of promoting intensive treatment for normoglycaemia. In comparison to that observed in standard treatment during the feasibility phase, the experimental group realized a higher rate of severe hypoglycaemic reactions, "defined as coma or seizure or a reaction requiring hospitalization or intravenous glucose or glucagon" (The DCCT Research Group, 1987, p. 4). The costs of care of severe hypoglycaemic events as well as their harm may counter any general advantage in promoting strict diabetic control to achieve normoglycaemia and reduce complications. Those conducting the trial have wisely noted " ... the need to determine whether the potential benefits of Intensive Treatment (i.e., delaying or preventing early vascular complications) will outweigh the increased risk of hypoglycemia with which it is associated" (The DCCT Research Group, 1987, p. 14).

In spite of the occurrence of severe hypoglycaemia observed in the feasibility phase, intensive treatment may still appear attractive. If it is possible to educate patients to prevent severe hypoglycaemic events, it may be possible to encourage intensive regimens for normoglycaemia without the costs of medical and hospital care of hypoglycaemia and its associated morbidity. If this were the case, efforts to encourage intensive treatment and strict control might yet be desirable from the perspective of reducing the costs and harm of diabetes.

Now let us view the desirability of intensive treatment *not* from the perspective of diabetes but from the perspective of those *with* diabetes. Here, a further finding from the feasibility phase is pertinent. In addition to the increased rate of severe hypoglycaemia associated with it, intensive treatment was also associated with a two- to three-fold increase in the rate of mild hypoglycaemia. Mild hypoglycaemia was defined liberally to include mere reports of such symptoms as sweating, hunger, or blurred vision (The DCCT Research Group, 1987, pp. 4–5). After 12 months of the feasibility study, observed rates of mild hypoglycaemia were 2.3 and 0.9 events per week with intensive and standard treatments, respectively. Note that these rates were observed over a 12-month feasibility phase. It is unlikely, therefore, that the rate among those using intensive treatment is attributable to their needing more time to master their more complicated regimen. Thus, the greater rate of mild hypoglycaemia with intensive treatment may represent a continuing cost of this treatment. It may be that a 30% reduction in the risk of retinopathy may come at a cost of a 255% increase in the frequency of mild hypoglycaemia or hypoglycaemic symptoms. Add to this the individual's time and effort necessary to carry out intensive treatment. Even if the costs and harm of severe hypoglycaemia may be avoidable, the advantages of intensive treatment become questionable.

When viewed from the perspective of the collectivity and its interests in reducing health-care costs, intensive treatment of diabetes to achieve normoglycaemia may be very attractive if the associated incidence of severe hypoglycaemia can be controlled. From the perspective of the person with diabetes, however, the costs of intensive treatment in time and effort and the associated impacts on quality of life of more frequent symptoms of hypoglycaemia may well outweigh the benefit of a 30% reduction in rates of retinopathy. The point of this example is not to resolve the utility of intensive treatment of diabetes, but to illustrate how the individual's perspective may differ from that of the group in evaluating the utility. We can see how one person's decision to use an intensive regimen and another's decision not to use such a regimen might both be wise, depending on individual circumstances and individual appraisals of the costs and benefits of different courses of action. (This example of the individual's perspective was suggested by Robert Kaplan, Ph.D., of the University of California at San Diego. Julio Santiago, M.D., of Washington University School of Medicine, provided much help in the description and interpretation of the feasibility phase of the Diabetes Control and Complications Trial.)

In establishing community health campaigns, we may emphasize the perspective of the person or that of the collective, depending on such factors as the severity of risk or the extent to which a programme intrudes on the other needs of the individual. At one extreme, we might say it is up to the diabetic person to decide whether to follow an aggressive regimen designed to achieve normoglycaemia. At the other extreme, regardless of whose perspective is taken, the disadvantages of smoking may so far outweigh its advantages that public policy can impose a moral imperative on the individual not to smoke. Where, however, should the line be drawn?

The emphasis on the perspective of the person is pertinent to current debate over such public health issues as confidentiality of tests for AIDS. Public disclosure of a positive test or even of having sought testing may seem to threaten terrible accusations from friends, employers, and even families. From the perspective of the person, the social and personal consequences of such accusations may well rival the utility of test results. Failing to consider this perspective can only result in policy which alienates those it needs to influence.

Discussion and Conclusions

Reviewing the three ethical issues considered, we can see that mobilizing a sense of community to face challenges to our health raises important issues regarding the rights of the individual versus those of society, the responsibility of individuals for the consequences of their lifestyles, and whether we choose our goals with sensitivity to the individual's perspective or only with concern for reducing the collective impact of a particular risk factor or disease. These ethical problems will never be completely solved. Nevertheless, two emphases may help guide us through them. The first is on a caring community. Risks, even lifestyle risks, emerge from forces beyond individual control. This places a very serious responsibility on all of us, on society, on the community, to assist those in need. No matter how we judge their actions, the things they have chosen, we must maintain a compassionate stance towards those who need help.

The emphasis on a caring community is consistent with the principle discussed above that we should act to expand the choices available to the individual. Helping the ill to recover, helping those whose capacities have been reduced by chronic disease to make the most of what ability they retain, or helping the educationally and economically disadvantaged to pursue healthier lifestyles — all may be viewed as increasing the availability of healthy alternatives to risky lifestyles.

The second emphasis which may guide us is respect for individuality and individual rights. In most areas which concern us as health professionals, there is great variability among individuals and what individuals value. Consequently, we must develop community health programmes which still encourage individuals to develop their own lifestyles through their own choices. Putting the importance of individual rights in a more positive way, we must mobilize the community, while ensuring respect for the individual rights of those who comprise it.

If we act with emphasis on mutual assistance and the rights of individuals, we can develop community health programmes which effectively mobilize the efforts of citizens. Such an approach can best meet the challenge of AIDS, by encouraging widespread efforts to control transmission and by treating as best we can those who become afflicted with the disease. Similarly, we shall best encourage widespread community support for the goal of a smoke-free society if we respect the rights of all citizens, nonsmokers and smokers, and if we offer as much

171

help and education as we can to smokers and those who are liable to become smokers.

Connected to both the nature of a caring community and respect for individuality, the responsibility of the individual remains a difficult issue. We associate treating the individual with respect with treating the individual as responsible. Yet, the individual's choices may be viewed as determined by forces over which he or she has little control. How can we resolve the conflict between treating individuals with respect and not holding them responsible for their actions? One solution to this may lie with the concept of the availability of alternatives, discussed earlier. We may come to terms with individual responsibility by working to make more *available* those habits and choices we hold to be responsible. Safe sexual practices may be the responsibility of those who are sexually active outside long-term, monogamous relationships. If so, we need to increase the availability of responsible practices through education, public information about condom use, access to testing and counselling, and community programs to encourage actual practice of safe habits. If some groups do not act responsibly, we should identify and correct those factors which limit the availability to them of responsible actions. Increasing the availability of responsible behaviour is more ethical and likely to be more effective than punishing its absence. As a caring community, we can promote those conditions which encourage responsible behaviour rather than imposing excessive fines or taxes in the name of responsibility.

Individual responsibility may be reconstrued as something the community encourages rather than something it merely expects. This requires that we identify what actions we shall judge responsible and what is required to make those actions available. We must then act as a community to meet those requirements of responsible behaviour. All of this places great *responsibility* on the community. Indeed, individual responsibility and community responsibility are interdependent.

In our eagerness to reduce risks, we must keep in mind that risks are not people. We may tend to identify others in terms of their risks as, e.g., smokers, Type A personalities, or homosexuals. However, when we take their perspective, we recognize that smoking, Type A habits, and homosexuality are things they do, not them. A habit of a person is a part of his or her life, not the whole of it. Public policy should be designed to combat tobacco smoking, not smokers. In setting public policy regarding the *actions* people choose, such as smoking, frequent changes in sex partners, or poor blood glucose control, we need to confine our attention to actions which are of true health significance, not take the whole lifestyle of the person making the choice.

Because AIDS in the USA has been associated with stigmatized sexual practices and drug addiction, many still view it as a moral issue. Frightened by AIDS and understanding neither its transmission nor that it is a threat to us all, some confuse risk factors with entire lifestyles or even with the people pursuing the lifestyles. They try to fight AIDS by condemning, controlling, segregating, or eliminating lifestyles and

172

people they associate with risk of AIDS. Of course, efforts to combat AIDS by segregating or punishing those at risk will most likely drive away those who need help and whose cooperation society needs.

Distinguishing between risk factors and the lifestyles with which they may be associated highlights an interesting interaction between scientific understanding and ethics. As we gain precision in our knowledge of risks, we can place values on those habits which are of actual harm, not the more general habits or lifestyles with which they may be associated. In fighting AIDS, we need to focus attention on the risks of unsafe sexual habits and sharing intravenous needles, not homosexuality and drug addiction.

A final consideration is the role in public health of moral judgments about individual behaviour. We tend to devote great energy to negative judgments of lifestyles or groups we associate with risks or immoral practices. As a caring community with respect for individuality, perhaps we can talk more about what morality in intimacy should entail. Perhaps we can base moral judgments on the characteristics of the intimacy between two people rather than on their sexual identities. The threat of AIDS may make us more aware that intimate relationships should include caring and acting with responsibility towards those for whom we care. Caring may take many forms, towards many different types of people, for short or long periods of time. Each of these forms may be borne with responsibility to our partners and, thereby, to the community. Of course, morality cannot promise the complete avoidance of risk. Given our current knowledge and available technology, there may be no absolutely safe sex in our culture. But then the wise have long recognized that all intimacy entails a variety of risks.

It is interesting to consider the parallels between the importance of caring and responsibility in intimate relationships and the sense of community in health programmes. Caring for one another and responsibility to one another may be not only the corner-stones of intimate relationships but also the bases of a sense of community. Here, there is an important parallel between ethics in community health promotion and ethics in relationships. As they are central to relationships which may help halt the spread of AIDS, mutual caring and mutual responsibility also may stand as important principles for our culture in its response to AIDS.

References

Begin, M. (1987). *Lifestyles and health hazards: individual choices and collective interests.* Paper presented at XXIst Conference of Council for International Organizations of Medical Sciences, "Health Policy, Ethics and Human Values." Noordwijk aan Zee, The Netherlands, 2–5 June.

Blair, A. *et al.* (1980). Physical, psychological, and sociodemographic differences among smokers, ex-smokers, and nonsmokers in a working population. *Preventive Medicine*, **9**, 747–759.

The DCCT Research Group. (1986). The Diabetes Control and Complications Trial (DCCT): Design and methodologic considerations for the Feasibility Phase. *Diabetes, 35,* 530–545.

The DCCT Research Group. (1987). Diabetes Control and Complications Trial (DCCT): Results of Feasibility Study. *Diabetes Care, 10,* 1–19.

Department of Health and Human Services. (1987). *Smoking and Health: A National Status Report: A Report to Congress.* Washington D.C., DHHS (CDC) Publication No. 87–8396.

Fisher, E.B., Jr. (1982). Prevention in Adulthood: Self-Motivate Quitting. In: *The Health Consequences of Smoking: Cancer: A Report of the Surgeon General.* Washington D.C., DHHS (PHS) Publication No. 82–50179. Department of Health and Human Services.

Fisher, E.B. Jr., & Rost, K. (1986). Smoking Cessation: A Practical Guide for the Physician, *Clinics in Chest Medicine, 7,* 551–565.

Friedman, G.D. *et al.* (1979). Characteristics predictive of coronary heart disease in ex-smokers before they stopped smoking: Comparison with persistent smokers and nonsmokers. *Journal of Chronic Diseases, 32,* 175–190.

Gorovitz, S. (1987). *Interactions of Health Policy, Ethics and Human Values: A North American Perspective.* Paper presented at XXIst Conference of Council for International Organizations of Medical Sciences, "Health Policy, Ethics and Human Values." Noordwijk aan Zee, The Netherlands, 2–5 June.

Knowles, J.H. (December 16, 1977). Responsibility for health. [Editorial]. *Science,* **198**.

Koop, C.E. *Surgeon General's Report on Acquired Immune Deficiency Syndrome.* U.S. Department of Health and Human Services.

Koop, C.E. (1986). *The Health Consequences of Smoking: Cancer and Chronic Lung Disease in the Workplace: A Report of the Surgeon General.* Washington D.C., DHHS (PHS), Pubication No. 86–0–157–964.

Perri, M.G. *et al.* (1977). Behavioral self-control and smoking reduction: A study of self-initiated attempts to reduce smoking. *Behavior Therapy, 8,* 360–365.

Skinner, B.F. (1965). *Science and Human Behavior.* New York: The Free Press.

174

Life Styles and Health Hazards

Report of Discussion Group

E. Fisher

Central to this summary is a consensus definition of lifestyle developed by the working group on Lifestyles and Health Hazards. We defined lifestyle as including physical and psychological behaviours, habits, and practices that imply an element of personal choice. The words "element" and "imply" are both important. Some of us view personal choice as an attractive myth amidst the reality of determinism of human behaviour. Others view personal choice as real, as reflecting some element of self-determination, albeit surrounded by strong forces that may minimize it. Thus, we agree that personal choice is but an *element* in the individual's activities. Some of us see lifestyle as *imply*ing personal choice as a real cause of behaviour while others see only the implication of a pleasing myth.

Despite our differences over the metaphysics of personal choice, we all agreed that, for the purposes of this conference, we should exclude frankly environmental factors such as air pollution from our definition of lifestyle.

Key Issues

We focused on a number of key issues. Among them was, as reflected in our plenary sessions, the issue of individual and group rights. This includes interests, duties and responsibilities of the group and individual and, in some cases, tensions between the rights, etc. of the individual and of the group.

Another key issue was the idea that quality of life should include a range of lifestyle choices.

A third key issue was the importance of public access to meaningful information about health and lifestyles. This requires public access to education to equip the public to make use of meaningful information. Making sense of weekly newspaper articles about health and lifestyles requires education which may not be widely available in our culture.

We entertained repeated discussion of the nature of health. Some participants viewed health as an overall and primary goal. Others viewed it as a means to the achievement of other ends. Some of us viewed it as a general abstraction which encompasses our lives and their planning and development.

There was general attention to the importance of scientific, rational, or empirical grounding of both the goals of interventions and the plans for pursuing them. Good intentions alone do not justify or validate the ethics of a programme or policy.

Our group was generally sympathetic to the idea that we should at all times be tolerant and understanding of our own and our fellows' weaknesses. Nevertheless, we also realized that some conditions and factors may be, indeed, intolerable. That is, some lifestyle choices may be so destructive as to justify infringing on individual prerogatives or punishing individuals who persist in these choices. However, I think we felt so much in awe of the task of reaching consensus as to what might be the criteria of "intolerable" or what might be some "intolerable" habits that we did not attempt to reach it.

Finally, we recognized that social, political and economic factors stand as an important background to individuals' lifestyles. All of these are key issues, not consensus points.

Policy Recommendations

We did have several policy recommendations. First, government and other institutions in our cultures should be sensitive to the fact that reduced access to care and other problems are often confined to specific groups with unique needs. An example is anorexia nervosa, which is almost totally limited to adolescent and teenage women. Young women with anorexia nervosa have needs and concerns that are quite specific to their problem. Their problems concern culturally transmitted distortions of physical attractiveness, as well as personal identity, control of one's own body and life, and sexuality. Young women inclined to anorexia nervosa are not going to be aided by lectures on the advantages to cardiovascular health of maintaining ideal body-weight.

A second policy recommendation was that policy should be pursued with recognition that there are multiple avenues of intervention and with recognition of the need for a long-term perspective in understanding interventions. These two characteristics of health interventions may seem unrelated. Both derive from the general idea that interventions aimed at lifestyles will have complex effects as they influence the complex personal factors that are connected to our lifestyles. Because of this complexity intrinsic to lifestyle interventions, their effects may take some time to manifest. There are several important dimensions of this recommendation. One is that simply evaluating a policy or an initiative by its results over six months or a year is unsatisfactory. Changes in behaviour and in lifestyles are aggregate phenomena. They take place over extended periods of time and are the results of many interventions. As an example, consider an individual participating in a group smoking cessation clinic. Success may be dependent in part on a government pamphlet read five years earlier which sensitized the quitter to some important ideas about risks in smoking. Yet, no evaluation of such a pamplet is likely to have captured this kind of impact.

Third, there was general consensus that access to care should not be based on lifestyle. We discussed at length the proposition that persistence in voluntary risks might disqualify a person for some types of care.

For instance, continuing to smoke in spite of current educational campaigns about the risks of smoking might disqualify one for costly, extended care for diseases related to smoking. The consensus *against* such disqualifications seemed quite determined and resilient.

We also made a wide-ranging recommendation that governments and other organizations in our cultures should take steps to:

(1) encourage the generation of reliable and scientific knowledge regarding health, behavioural risk factors, and change of behavioural risk factors

(2) restrict behaviours which burden health and the health-care system

(3) restrict behaviours which burden the health of others

(4) restrict corporate and individual practices which might interfere with healthy lifestyles

(5) promote conditions which enhance the ability of individuals to pursue healthy lifestyles.

Another policy recommendation was to amend Article 12 of the International Covenant on Economic, Social, and Cultural Rights to include explicit recognition of the individual's right to information about factors affecting health and lifestyles in our societies.

Our final policy recommendation was a methodological one. Health policies and initiatives should be based on empirical, rational bases, including evaluation. This goes back to the key point that good intentions are not sufficient guarantees of the ethics of health policies.

Unanswered Questions

We also tried to identify what we considered to be important unanswered questions. We recognized that our discussion made frequent reference to values we assume without question to be important, such as personal freedom, social responsibility, individual responsibility, and mutual assistance. However, we also recognized conflicts among these values, which seem difficult to resolve. Indeed, health problems accentuate conflict among values which seem, in themselves, unassailable. There is a need for new ethical and philosophical models to link or integrate or, perhaps, transcend these classical values.

A second group of important unanswered questions surrounds the effects of social institutions on lifestyles and health. Here, we define social institutions broadly to include families, work-places, government, peer groups, etc. These effects have important ethical implications. For instance, evidence that smoking is influenced by economic and social factors casts doubt on the attribution to free will of the choice to smoke.

Trends in Analysis

Finally, we noted several trends in our thinking about lifestyle modification that seemed important to us. First is recognition of the great variability among lifestyles, cultures, health promotion programmes, and paths to desirable changes. We recognized that our cultures need to respect and accommodate the variety of values and perspectives on health among their members. As there is great variability among lifestyles, so there are many ways to encourage lifestyle changes. Interventions in clinical settings will reach many individuals, but so will educational programmes in mass media. Very likely, any individual's change is a response to a variety of influences, from the standards of the peer group to the warning of the health professional. No single programme is adequate to all cases. No one programme is sufficient, in itself. Rather, an adequate approach to lifestyle risk reduction needs to include many different programmes and procedures to suit individual needs and styles of changing behaviour.

Parallel to variability among ways of promoting change is variability among paths by which individuals change their lifestyles. Some may make several sweeping changes at once while others make small changes over an extended period. Some enlist the help of family and friends while others prefer solitary effort. There is great variability among individual goals, cultural values, effective interventions, and individual responses to health promotion programmes. This variability is the nature of lifestyle and lifestyle change. Articulating this variability does not reflect imprecise knowledge of the field. Rather it reflects adequate knowledge of the nature of lifestyles.

As our discussion recognized the variability in lifestyle and lifestyle change, so it also recognized models of multi-causality of problems. Lifestyles and behaviour are multiply determined, by a variety of forces. From this is derived the need for multiple approaches to encouraging change in lifestyles, as noted above. Risk factors also operate in a manner best described as multi-causal—no single risk factor is sufficient or necessary for most diseases related to lifestyles. As causation is multi-faceted, so there is increasing scientific understanding of the interplay of biological and social factors in the development of both risks and diseases.

REFLECTIONS AND PERSPECTIVES

The Viewpoint of the Health Policymaker

E. W. Roscam Abbing*

As the first in a long series of speakers, I shall try to elaborate the standpoints of the policymaker in respect to bioethics and I shall work out especially the relation between the policymaker and the ethicist. First, however, I want to present to you an imaginary case, just to bring together the four themes we have been studying during the last few days.

Take the case of Mr V.I.P. who has already lived 70 years and is now rather ill with cirrhosis of the liver. He has been a very meritorious member of society. He was a politician and a successful entrepreneur; he made an enormous financial fortune, and is still of great importance to society. But during his very busy, stressful life, he began to drink, went on to drink heavily and became an alcoholic, with disastrous results for his liver. You have already noticed three of our themes, but not the fourth — the theme of screening. In the past, when our patient was 40 years old and an active politician, he promoted a screening programme on genetic disposition to alcoholism, and he himself got a positive result. He had this disposition, but it did not prevent him from drinking.

We have so far used three ethical principles to assess this case: the principle of autonomy, linked with good information; the principle of doing no harm; and, thirdly the principle of equity (justice and fairness).

I shall now try to scrutinize, to assess, this case, first from the patient's viewpoint. He thinks, on the basis of his autonomy and being well-informed on the possibilities, that he is in a good position to apply for a liver transplant. He thinks he is doing nobody any harm — the donor cannot be harmed any more — the donor will be dead. He thinks there is some fairness in it. He was a good, active member of society and his working style, unluckily, led to his heavy drinking, but this was only the result of a very stressful life. He thinks he is entitled to a liver transplant.

Now let us consider the standpoint of the doctor. He has his doubts. Of course he respects his patient's autonomous decision, and of course he has some respect for Mr V.I.P. He does not believe the man would stop drinking after an operation and, moreover, he knows that the patient's age is a great risk. With regard to equity, he knows that this man is well insured and has already paid his financial tribute to solidarity and even more. Nevertheless, he is in doubt.

Now the third standpoint, the one I want to elaborate, is the standpoint of society, or representatives of society — governments, and I shall restrict myself to central governments, because of my own position. The case poses many problems. First of all, central government does not

* Deputy Director-General of Health, Ministry of Welfare, Health and Cultural Affairs, Rijswijk, Netherlands.

have to become involved with an individual case. Central government does not try to decide upon individual cases but leaves it to patients and doctors, depending upon the system, a bit more the patient or a bit more the doctor, but both are very important in such a type of decision. However, central government is concerned in a more general sense. Central government sets certain limits on the autonomy of citizens. Very difficult questions arise. Could there ever be, for instance, a general age criterion? Could there be such a criterion as social value, but also a criterion that takes account of people who neglect warnings, who do not take into account what they know very well about lifestyles? Could there be some general criterion for the consequences? We have been discussing these matters in much more detail in the last few days.

The second principle "do no harm" is, at the macro-level, a concern of the doctor rather than the patient. For the doctor there is already the consideration that other people on his waiting list cannot be displaced by Mr V.I.P. For the government, however, for society as a whole, this question of allocation of possibilities, of money, of facilities, is a very concrete and difficult one, with ethical implications; it encompasses the second and third ethical principles — doing no harm and equity. The principle of fair distribution of possibilities always arises in decisions about distribution, in decisions about planning and about the allocation of money, and so on. Such a case makes it clear to government that it cannot stand off at a great distance from ethical, bioethical, questions. All four themes which we have discussed during the last few days are also of importance to the policymaker.

Let me get away from this imaginary case to the more general problem of the relation between policymakers or government and ethicists. The relation is twofold: first, government should pay attention to ethical, bioethical, questions; and, secondly, government can pay proper attention to bioethics only if it respects the principles of the ethics of decision-making, of policymaking. This means that government has to respect the rules of the democratic system, to take into account the standpoints of minorities in society, to be fair in using ethical arguments, to not use ethical arguments in a merely opportunistic sense, just for momentary, electoral results, or to flatter the electorate, etc. Such ethical questions are always present in policymaking and in politics.

It is possible to take proper account of arguments of bioethics only if the ethics of policymaking itself is taken seriously. How can policy-makers be serious about ethical arguments, and especially bioethical arguments? I think there should be a continuous dialogue with the other parties, with researchers, the scientific workers in the ethical field, but also with health care professionals and with the organizations of patients. All these parties must be consulted by government in a more systematic way than any we have at hand at the moment. This means that government must scrutinize its own decision-making procedures in the light of ethics and must have the courage to ask for advice in matters that have a highly ethical content; I am fully aware that almost all policymaking has its ethical aspects, and for that reason everything should be scrutinized in this way. Certainly a more systematic approach in those cases with very evident ethical implications would already be an advance compared with our methods today.

Governments could promote a more systematic approach to ethical questions in other ways. Not only could they seek advice, and consult professionals, doctors and patients; but also they could set up a research programme in the ethical field that would not be merely opportunistic, that would not be founded only on transitory concerns of society, but that would be more systematic. To my knowledge, there is no such programme, but one could be worked out. We could, I think, enable government to devise a more systematic approach to ethics by establishing a research programme that would address these issues.

I now come to our conference. I think there must be an international dimension to ethics in policymaking. Let us take the peculiar situation that people come to the Netherlands from abroad, from Belgium for example, who want to have an abortion here. But, at the same time, Dutch people are going to Belgium for *in vitro* fertilization. Clearly, there is an international dimension to the question and government should promote both national and international discussion about it. Policymakers do have a responsibility in this respect.

The Viewpoint of the Health Professional

S. Doxiadis*

I have been asked to present the viewpoint of a health professional who is also sometimes a researcher. In this respect, what he can do for the ethical issues is to bring his analytical, his scientific, methodology to bear on problems which are usually not subjected to such scrutiny. But health professionals act mainly as providers of services, providers of care, and it is in this respect that they face ethical problems. Health professionals are not only doctors but also many other kinds of health-care worker, and most of those who may be faced with ethical questions work in primary care. It is on this sector of health services that we have to focus our attention. Most of the work done in modern teaching hospitals has become so specialized and subdivided that the last generalist remaining in them is the patient.

Now, I have the good fortune to be, and to have been, a primary-care physician, a hospital doctor, a teacher and a researcher, but I have the bad luck to be asked to express reflections and to offer suggestions after three days of a very rich programme involving many subjects, many disciplines. My viewpoint inevitably, as regards the present conference, is influenced by the discussions of the group to which I was assigned — the group on screening and counselling. Many of you may think that I belong much more to group 3 — that of the elderly. This, however, depends on how you look at age. Age is a very relative thing.

I shall now offer some observations which contain suggestions in order to help CIOMS conferences and mainly our very hardworking Dr Bryant and Dr Bankowski, who organized in such a splendid way the present conference and to whom I am personally very grateful for being asked to come here and also to the WHO European Office for making it possible.

Some general observations about this conference. Sometimes the description of a problem was considered as the main objective of a discussion. It did not end with bringing to the surface the ethical issues arising during daily practice and, if there were some conclusions from the field of ethics, these were more a tendency to establish a moral code rather than to initiate an ethical analysis. But, unless we initiate ethical analysis, moral codes become ossified, and for the health professional it is important to make him start thinking, not applying moral codes.

Another observation relates to differences in emphasis or in priorities. In our discussions the priorities did not reflect the priorities of the practice of health care, because these priorities must depend on how frequent a problem is and how damaging to health is the condition we are discussing. This gap in priorities between our discussions and day-to-day practice is due to two causes.

---

* President, Foundation for Research in Childhood, Athens, Greece.

The first is the lure of technological progress. Teachers and researchers are always eager to be among the first to exploit the possibilities afforded by new knowledge and new technology, and they discard objectives which may be approached by old methods. For example, there are many health problems which require ethical analysis but the problems as such cannot be investigated by modern technological methods but by the old methods of interviews, of questionnaires, of the human approach. This brings us to the second cause for this gap, and this is that many, especially academic, doctors are afraid of soft data. They feel insecure. They prefer to ignore fields in which no hard data can be found and they prefer a rare disease because it can be approached through modern technology. They tend therefore to neglect very common problems, but problems cannot wait. Patients come every day and they present themselves to the health professional, and he has to find solutions and to give answers. He cannot tell them: "Wait until we have more hard data on your condition". And often these types of problems are ethically much more difficult to analyse than are rare diseases.

I will repeat the examples I brought to our group discussion, one of which was the subject of the previous CIOMS conference — child abuse.

Child abuse and neglect create many ethical problems but we have not got a modern instrument with which to approach them. We have to go through old methods, and therefore many people tend to forget the existence of this type of problem or others, such as, for example, drug abuse. In the field of child abuse, how many ethical problems exist if you want to investigate a family and find out whether a child has been physically abused, emotionally neglected or, even worse, sexually abused. And if you want to prevent child abuse and therefore try to find the "at risk" families, think how difficult or how ethically possible it is to go and investigate family conditions? How permissible is it to go and ask the neighbours about a certain family? Because there are no other ways to approach this type of problem. And then if you do find that a child is abused or neglected think of the ethical issues in the intervention of the health and the social services.

We have to bear in mind therefore that, mainly, common problems should be investigated. We should be more sensitive to the ethical problems arising in day-to-day practice. This means that we should not forget these problems, because they are the more difficult. They may appear to the academic doctor to be outside his field of interest. But to the ethical analyst and to the health professional, they are very important and we have to switch our attention to this type of common problem.

I have to finish now with some suggestions for all of us. These will be: one thing to avoid, one thing to respect, and three needs to recognize.

The thing to avoid: Avoid *groupings and generalizations*, because there is such an enormous variation in the severity of conditions and problems. To talk, for example, as we have done, about "handicapped people" means nothing because there is a wide range of handicaps and we have to recognize the uniqueness of each problem.

The thing to respect is individuality. In the International Year of the Child (1979), I was asked to give the Ciba Foundation lecture of the year and I chose as my subject "The Right to Be Different". This was not very well accepted. But it is something we have to realize and accept: the right of everyone to be different. An example would be the age of consent of a minor for something. For some children it might be 12 years, for others 10, for others 14. Obviously, by law we have to accept some generalizations and dividing lines, but for each individual child the age of consent is different. Or, take the other extreme. In my country we have quite often at our birthdays a wish which in English would be translated: "May you reach 100 years". So everybody accepts this wish without much thought until the age of 60 or 65. After this age everybody says "Well, let's hope I will reach 100". But, a man of 94, when someone wished him on his birthday "May you reach 100" was upset. He said "You only give me six more years? Why?" So you see how the point you stand on makes such a difference.

Now to *the three needs* for all of us. We need much more *risk assessment* if we want an ethical analysis. We need much more *auditing of our actions* and we need much clearer *distinction between a scientific issue and an ethical issue*, because sometimes we confuse these two.

To return to the health professional -- his duties and his needs. What has he to offer? The human touch. But he has also to be an educator, an educator not only of his patients, not only of the community he works in, but also of political leaders. They will accept better some advice, some education, from their own personal physician than from an academic doctor. But also he has to educate politicians by increasing demand among the public, because politicians are very sensitive to demands from the public.

What does the health professional need? Much more basic training. Medical training in ethics is now in many countries where psychology or social medicine was 20 years ago. We just start now in many medical schools to think about the need of the health professional to get some basic instruction in ethics and in moral codes, and he will have to be trained to keep always an open mind. New problems arise all the time and we cannot solve them with moral codes founded before their appearance. We have to keep an open mind in order to be able to analyse them from an ethical point of view.

185

The Viewpoint of the Ethicist

S. Gorovitz*

I have been asked to provide "reflections, implications, suggestions and conclusions" on the entire meeting, from the "the viewpoint of the ethicist," and to do it in 15 minutes. I asked for extra time — for two days — but I was told, "Possibly 17 minutes." So I propose merely to offer a few opinions as one moral philosopher — that is, as a philosopher with an interest in moral questions — about some of the issues that arise in the context of medicine, health care, and health policy.

It might be useful to characterize more explicitly at the outset what I mean by moral or ethical questions. These questions concern value issues, the most fundamental principles of how people should act towards one another — questions of justice, of what it is to respect one another, of what goals are most worth pursuing, of what makes right acts right and wrong acts wrong, of what it means to be a member of the human community and of what obligations we have as members of a social order. These are the types of question on the ethical agenda.

We have considered four specific topics, related to transplantation, genetics, the elderly, and "lifestyle." In respect to lifestyle, we have been dealing primarily with behaviours that are destructive of optional health. Before commenting on what these four different areas have in common, I want to note one feature of health policy in general and say something about what moral philosophers do.

Health policy is inherently a value-laden enterprise. Every health policy is driven by assumptions about what ends are worth seeking, what constraints must be respected, what means are justified, what is most important. These assumptions are often, and perhaps even typically, unstated and unexamined, but they are always present. For example, we could eliminate the dreadful health consequences of smoking simply by making the use of tobacco a capital offence. But, on moral grounds, we would not do so. We could eliminate the problem of financing health care for the elderly by simply prohibiting treatment of anyone over 80 years of age. But, on moral grounds, we would not do so. We could eliminate the shortage of organs for transplantation simply by making cadaver organs immediately the property of the State. But, on moral grounds, we would not do so. And there are obviously moral constraints on our use of the techniques of contemporary genetics.

The role of the moral philosopher or "ethicist" is not to provide moral authority. Those of us in the ethics business are not high priests of ethical expertise, with sets of answers just awaiting the policymakers' questions. Our role, instead, is to help analyse the moral content of policies, of

---

* Dean, College of Arts and Sciences, Syracuse University, Syracuse, New York, U.S.A.

situations, and of arguments. The kinds of questions that we seek to answer about any health policy, actual or contemplated, are these: What values motivate this policy? What values does this policy serve? Are they the same or do they diverge? Are the values explicit, resulting from reflection and analysis, or are they simply assumed, conventional values? And so on. For example, we point out that respect for the dignity and autonomy of individual persons requires us to allow people to smoke, so long as they do not do it in the presence of unconsenting non-smokers. (That, I believe, is a genuinely immoral act.) And it requires us to allow people to refuse to donate their organs. It also requires us to care for those in need, whatever their age. At the same time, we point out that total freedom is not an ideal, it is a contradiction. No one is free except in a social context of mutual rights, limitations, and responsibilities. But what these responsibilities are and how they affect health policy is an exceedingly complex question.

Now, to our four areas. In each we can see the tension between individual and collective interests. In each there is an agenda of ethical questions that arise as we seek to identify the best health policies to support. For example, how should we rate the need of one patient against that of another, when the first has a transplanted organ that is failing, while the second is awaiting a first transplant? Or, how should we handle genetic information about a patient who wants it kept from a spouse, to whom it is vitally important? Or, how should we advise a physician who just wants to dismiss and stop treating a frustrating patient with emphysema, who refuses to stop smoking? And yesterday, Dr Callahan gave us a superb overview of a long list of ethical problems related to the notion of the elderly.

What each of these areas has in common is that value questions are pervasive within it. Further, they are not the sort of questions, these value questions, that can be answered in any stable, absolute way. Ethical judgement is not independent of what is going on in the world. Indeed, it is *about* what is going on in the world. Since what goes on in the world of health care is ever-changing and the process of health policy formation is unending, there is a continuing need for ethical analysis as part of the basic process of health policymaking.

On Tuesday, I presented some examples of policy situations of a variety of kinds — the successful, the inevitably unsuccessful, the unnecessarily unsuccessful, and the partially successful. What accounts for the differences among these examples is not a question of technical expertise, available resources, or medical progress. It is the difference in the extent to which the underlying values served by policy are in harmony with values of the social order. Since social values concerning abortion are in chaotic discord, no coherent policy can be in harmony with them. Since our values concerning treating human organs as market commodities are at present stable and coherent, it is possible to fashion a successful policy.

In each of the four areas we have been considering there are issues that can be resolved by remembering our traditional values of honesty, beneficence, respect for persons, and justice. But equally there arise issues that are new and which challenge our understanding of our own values. Our traditional values do not suffice, even when they are clear, to answer all the problems we face in health policy — not in the four areas we have considered, or in any other area. You cannot look up "organ donation" in the index of the Bible and find any useful advice. The Koran, if I am not mistaken, does not speak about the limits of genetic therapy. The works of Plato and Aristotle are silent on the use of life-extending therapies for VIVOs — that is, the very ill, very old.

Such sources give us guidance, but they always require, at the very least, controversial interpretation and extrapolation if they are to contribute to a satisfactory ethical analysis of a new problem in health policy. And such analysis requires hard, patient and careful work. It is no less demanding than economic, legal or any other important kind of analysis. This is why it is futile to seek much specific ethical clarification in the context of a conference like this one. Each specific issue requires separate, specific inquiry, separate reflection, separate debate — and these things take time and care.

The moral debate which led to the ban on kidney sales took only a few days in the public forums in the United States, but the participants in that debate had prepared for weeks. The discussions that have now paved the way for allowing limited trials of genetic therapy, when the techniques are ready for clinical trials, went on for well over a year before a clear consensus emerged about the moral limitations of this type of therapy.

It is quite reasonable for us to be content with our modest achievements in these few days. I, at least, have a clearer sense than I had before of many of the unanswered questions in each of the four areas. I also have clear evidence that the policymakers are sensitive to ethical concerns and want very much to take them into account. But it is equally clear that those who are practised in ethical analysis can contribute usefully to the process and that such collaboration can help policymakers serve the public interest.

There are many models of such collaboration. Multidisciplinary study commissions are one possible form, as are consulting arrangements — even from time to time having a philosopher working full-time on the staff of a health policy agency. I did that for a while in the Public Health Service in the United States and several other American philosophers have played that role in one federal or state agency or another.

In this setting, I cannot even begin to address the specific ethical questions raised by the four rapporteurs. But I yield to the temptation, in closing, of referring to one issue raised in the lifestyle group of which I was a part and addressed in plenary session by Dr Farber.

It is always difficult to strike a proper balance between the public interest and our desire to respect individual liberty, or between individual liberty and individual health. Some behaviours are provably dangerous or self-destructive, but we know that we must allow them all the same. I agree with Dr Farber that the physician has an obligation to treat the individual in a non-judgmental way in the face of illness or injury, however it was caused. It is not up to the physician to moralize to the patient about leading a virtuous life.

That said, I cannot ignore the suggestion that physicians have no further obligation with regard to prevention. Physicians are no experts in the moral life, but they do or should have specific knowledge about the relationships between various kinds of behaviour and various kinds of disease, and they ought to impart that knowledge when they can. To do so is not to advocate leading a dull life. One need not get on a motorcycle while dead drunk and ride around without a helmet, smoking cigars, in order to avoid a dull life. The opinion that one is no better off avoiding such imprudence, an opinion I now call "Farber's Fable", is not just amusing "bunk", it is dangerous "bunk". It can distract us from the importance of serious epidemiological evidence about the causes of disease, evidence that must be taken into account by any morally sound health policy and by any morally responsible health care provider.

The Perspective of the Developing World — Africa

B. O. Osuntokun*

I do not want to go into semantics about the definition of the developing world, but I think it is relevant to what I have to say. By and large, the developing countries have certain characteristics. Their resources for health care are very limited and inadequate. The social infrastructures which contribute to or influence health are also grossly inadequate. Poverty is widespread. Human misery is abundant. Some of this human misery is man-made. For example, it has been pointed out that since the Second World War, of the 145 wars fought in 82 countries, involving some 90 states, all have been in the developing world and one-third in the African countries. Because of competing demands we have to attend to what is needed by many rather than the demands of a few. What I have to say must be against the background of this picture of what we call the developing world.

The four themes of this conference, obviously of importance to the countries of the North, are also very relevant to the developing world of the South in the context of health policy, ethics and human values. It is true that, faced with dwindling or stagnant economic resources, and competing needs of enormous magnitude, the priorities of the developing world would differ from those of the developed countries. The methodological, technological and philosophical approach to solving problems may also differ.

The problems are, however, universal and some are of great magnitude in the developing world. Millions of people, mostly in the developing world, carry genes for the abnormal haemoglobins. In Nigeria alone, for example, a country with 100 million people, a quarter of the population of Africa, 25 million are heterozygous for the sickle-cell trait (and probably one million suffer from sickle-cell disease). The thalassaemic syndromes are widely distributed in the Middle East, India, South-East Asia, some parts of Africa and the West Indies (and, of course, in American Negroes). Carcinoma of the breast and of the cervix are common everywhere; they are the commonest malignancies in the female in sub-Saharan Africa. Hypertension afflicts 10–20% of the African Black. The issues of screening and counselling are as relevant to these diseases as they are to diseases elsewhere.

In developed countries, about 10% of the population is over the age of 65, compared with 5% in the developing world. However, over the next two decades, the population of the elderly is likely to increase more in the developing than in the developed world (Table 1).

---

* Professor, Department of Medicine, University of Ibadan, Ibadan, Nigeria.

191

Table 1*. Projected increase in the elderly population of the world

Area		Projected increase in the population aged 65 years and over, 1980–2000 (in millions)
The world		138
Developing		100
China	32	
India	17	
Other	51	
Developed		38
USSR	10	
USA	7	
Other	21	

*From WHO Technical Report Series, 706, 1984[1].

The world's population aged over 65 years was estimated at about 250 million in 1980, of which about 50% was in the developing countries. By the year 2000, with present trends in population increase, the number of people aged 65 years and more will reach 240 million in the developing countries and will greatly exceed the 166 million elderly in developed countries. The problems of the elderly will very soon be taxing the resources of the developing countries (which are undergoing epidemiological transition), where organization of social services is very rudimentary or non-existent and the extended family system, which has traditionally provided a buffer in the care of elderly, is being remorselessly dismantled. This has implications for health policymaking and ethics and human values.

The developing world, many parts of which have not yet eradicated or controlled infections and deficiency diseases, is now being threatened with the widespread occurrence of certain non-communicable diseases or "diseases of affluence" or "Western disease". These non-communicable diseases include hypertension, atherosclerosis and coronary artery disease, stroke, diabetes mellitus, some types of cancer and dental caries. Lifestyles have been shown to be important aetiological determinants of these diseases; they include smoking, sedentary living, reduced physical activity, use and abuse of drugs, including alcohol, and ill-balanced diets.

Organ transplantation is at present of less concern to the developing countries, for obvious reasons. But even they may benefit from consideration of some of the ethical issues being discussed, e.g., criteria for death as brain death, and cost-effectiveness and cost-benefit of transplantation of organs, such as the kidney, compared with other modes of treatment, including ambulatory peritoneal dialysis.

Primary Health Care: Topmost Priority in Developing Countries

To ensure equity and social justice with regard to the provision of health care, it is now generally agreed that the best approach is primary health care. In the context of primary health care, defined by WHO as "essential health care made universally accessible to individuals and families in the community by means acceptable to them, through their full participation and at a cost that the community and country can afford", the themes of the conference are also relevant. Some may question the appropriateness of organ transplantation in primary health care but there are ethical issues and concern with human values, particularly from the perspective of the donors, which are of great interest to the community. The ethical issues as related to health policy, in laying emphasis on primary health care, include the need to provide for the majority, satisfaction of the needs of the many rather than the demands of the few, and the necessity to use the limited resources of the developing world where they will yield the greatest good for the greatest number for the longest period. Moreover, planning health care delivery in the developing world must be based on economic grounds and increased efficiency.

Screening and Counselling

A few comments on screening and counselling. I believe the main thrust and objectives of screening are to achieve early detection, treatment and prevention of disease, and one may add promotion of health. Cost-effectiveness and cost-benefit are important considerations in communities with limited resources. For example, it may be relevant to know the number of quality-adjusted life years realised per unit of money spent in screening for cancer of the breast in a community, especially when compared with no screening programme (cost-effectiveness). Similarly, it is relevant to compare the cost of screening and effective treatment of hypertension with the cost and effectiveness of education (e.g. about reduced salt diet, physical exercise, avoidance of or coping with stress) in lowering the frequency of hypertension and its complications (cost-benefits).

In all countries, and especially in the developing countries, health policies should aim at an equitable balance of cost-effectiveness and cost-benefit in deciding on priorities in health care. For example, in developed countries, early detection and treatment by means of screening programmes have reduced the incidence of invasive cervical cancer, and in some countries the mortality attributable to the disease has fallen by as much as 60%. However, in the developing world, most screening programmes for cervical cancer reach only a small fraction of the population, usually young urban women, since screening is often linked to family planning campaigns. The effect on cervical cancer mortality is therefore marginal, since more than 90% of the tumours

193

occur in women over the age of 35 years. Screening may therefore be more cost-effective if the range of ages of women to be screened is changed to 35–55 in developed countries, from 20–65 in the developed world, and then re-screening is carried out every ten years instead of every two or three years.[2]

In determining health policy, the feasibility of treatment and prevention as a result of screening is important. It is unethical to screen a population where 10 to 20% of the population may be hypertensive, if all the hypertensives that require treatment cannot be offered adequate health care. Our experience in Nigeria has shown that those who do not know they are hypertensive prior to a screening programme would not accept treatment because of the unpleasant side-effects of drugs.

Screening and counselling for the sickle-cell trait present in 25% of a population is also, as regards cost-effectiveness, probably unethical. It is doubtful whether such a screening procedure is feasible, and whether individuals will accept counselling, e.g. about choice of or rejection of a marriage partner.

Screening for a rare disease or for one for which there is no effective treatment is unethical, and unjustifiable both economically and from the point of view of rational health policy. A polymorphic DNA marker may detect at-risk offspring of parents with Huntington's chorea, but is it ethical to inflict the consequent anxiety on such individuals years before they may show evidence of the disease? Of course, they may justifiably be advised not to have children.

There may be conflict between acting on the result of screening and an individual's religious or cultural belief, e.g., prenatal screening for developmental abormality of the fetus, and therapeutic termination of pregnancy in a Catholic community, which does not accept abortion.

Organ Transplantation

The issue of when to declare a person "brain-dead", so that life-support systems may be switched off to enable organs to be removed for transplantation, has aroused considerable debate in recent times. It would be useful to have international consensus on the definition of brain death. Many countries, such as the United Kingdom, rely almost entirely on clinical criteria. Others, Czechoslovakia and Sweden, for instance, require additional instrumental data (isoelectric EEG and non-filling of cerebral vasculature). Some countries, including some Islamic states, do not accept brain death as synonymous with death. When a television programme in one developed country in October 1980 suggested erroneously that organs could be removed from donors who were not really dead, several potential donors withdrew their consent.

As a result of cultural and religious beliefs, especially in the corporate existence of life after death, many people in some parts of the developing world would probably not agree to donate organs for transplantation. In Ibadan, Nigeria, a corneal transplant programme had to be abandoned because of lack of donors.

As I indicated earlier, organ transplantation is not a priority in health care in most parts of the developing world. The ethical issues were fully discussed by Abdussalam at the Athens (1984) Conference.[3]

The Elderly

The elderly are normally much adored, respected and valued in the developing world, and cared for by the entire family. They are not looked upon as being non-productive and hence not worthy of care. However, the social and health care infrastructure in most parts of the developing world does not adequately provide for support of the elderly or for solving their medical, mental and socioeconomic problems. The elderly often have to depend on the children and other members of the family. Unfortunately, the extended family system which has made it possible for the elderly to be looked after is gradually being dismantled and replaced by the nuclear family.

The quality of life is considered most important. Many cultures in the developing world believe in the concept that death can be honourable, and such honourable death is preferred to suffering and ignominy.

In the interest of social justice and equity, health policy in the developing world must take account of the ethics and the problems of caring for the elderly, with or without the support of the family. At present, in most countries, such a plan or a scheme does not exist.

Lifestyles

Alcohol abuse has become one of the world's most serious problems, putting intolerable strain on the home, the health services and industry. Alcohol is said to be the world's biggest killer after cancer and cardiovascular disease.

Alcohol consumption is increasing rapidly in some developing countries, as are its somatic and mental consequences. Nigeria's production of beer rose from 1.3 million litres in 1972 to 132 million litres in 1976, and 280 million litres in 1986. A recent report by the International Labour Organization showed that over the last 20 years the consumption of beer has increased worldwide by 124%, of wine by 20%, and of spirits by 50%. The medical costs of the ill-health caused by alcoholic beverages is much higher than the tax collected by governments on their sale. Apart from medical and mental diseases caused by alcohol, there are socioeconomic disadvantages, caused by abnormally high absenteeism from work, accidents and lower productivity. These are important considerations in formulating health policies.

The epidemic of tobacco smoking has spread into the developing world, and Third-World smoking, with aggressive, unfettered marketing by the tobacco companies, has been described as the new slave trade. Tobacco smoking in the industrialized world is falling by about 1%

annually but consumption in the developing countries is rising by about 2%. This is due largely to unbridled, uncontrolled advertising. In Kenya, tobacco sales are growing by 8% per annum, with the fastest growth among the educated 25- to 35-year-old men. A recent report states that 25% of Nigerian schoolchildren smoke cigarettes.

Tobacco-related diseases have begun to appear in the developing world, where they were previously rare. Cancer of the lung has been uncommon in the developing world, but now high death rates are reported from India, Hong Kong (where rates for women are the world's highest) and China and in South African Blacks in Natal; cases are being reported also from developing countries in tropical Africa and tropical America. It is now known that "passive smoking" is harmful.

The developing world needs to take steps to control and, if possible, stop the advertising of tobacco products. It is noteworthy that in the United States of America, a developed country, an attempt is being made to prohibit by law all advertising of tobacco, "the leading cause of premature death, a product so pervasive and lethal that it causes more deaths than the combined total caused by all illicit drugs and alcohol, all accidents, all homicides and suicides".[4]

Drug abuse is also widespread in the developing world. The current world-wide attempt to curb it is most welcome and should be supported by all governments.

A nutritional policy for health appears to be essential. Nutrition is probably the most important determinant of the health of a community. According to an eminent authority (Sir Richard Doll), when the objective is to avoid cancer, coronary heart disease, diabetes, diverticular disease, duodenal ulcer or constipation, there is broad agreement among research workers that the type of diet that is least likely to cause disease is one that provides a high proportion of calories in whole-grain cereals, vegetables and fruit, provides most of its animal protein in fish and poultry, limits the intake of fats and, if oils are to be used, gives preference to liquid vegetables oils, includes very few dairy products, eggs and little refined sugar.[5]

I think we have to accept Crew's postulate that "the therapeusis of Social Medicine is not medical but social and political action based upon medical recommendations".[6] It is ethical to take some statutory decisions, for example, to ban smoking in all public places and public transport. It is ethical and compatible with human values to mount a vigorous health education campaign to encourage citizens in spite of the sceptics to adopt healthy dietary habits. The developing world should be aware of the need to base health policies on medical and technological advances, and it is important that the providers of health care should take steps to educate individuals, communities and policymakers about what is known and how it can be applied to what is needed.

Finally, I believe that the perspective of the developing countries on these issues must take into consideration the limited resources and competing demands, and the priorities as determined by these developing countries. It is important to ensure social justice and equity; one way of doing so is to provide effective and efficient health care. We must recognize the individual's right to choose, but I think this must be subsumed within the larger rights of the community. The preference should be for measures that yield the greatest good for the largest number for the longest period: for example, fluoridation of community water supplies is justifiable as a health policy to prevent dental caries in spite of protests by individuals who may worry about fluoridosis. There is also the importance of the promotional role of the providers of health care. Our choice and our policies must be influenced by epidemiological considerations. I have referred to some of these (e.g. cancer of the cervix). Of course, we cannot ignore the culture and beliefs of people in the developing countries.

The developing world should be aware of the need to base health policy on medical and technological advances, about which individuals and communities should be adequately informed so as to derive maximum benefit from them.

References

[1] WHO Technical Report Series, No. 706, 1984 (*The uses of epidemiology in the study of the elderly:* report of a WHO Scientific Group) Geneva, World Health Organization, p. 9.

[2] Stjernsward, J. *et al.* Plotting a new course for cervical cancer screening in developing countries. *World Health Forum,* 8: 42–5 (1987).

[3] Abdussalam, M. Organ substitution therapy in the developing world: from corneal grafting to renal dialysis. *In:* Bankowski, Z. & Bryant, J.H. (ed.) *Health policy, ethics and human values: an international dialogue.* XVIIth CIOMS Round Table Conference, Geneva, CIOMS, 1985 (pp. 217–25).

[4] Warner, K.E. A ban on the promotion of tobacco products. *New England Journal of Medicine,* 316: 745–7 (1987).

[5] Doll, R. Prospects for prevention. *British Medical Journal,* 286: 445–53 (1983).

[6] Crew, F.A.E. *Measurement of the public health.* London, Oliver and Boyd, 1948, p. XI.

The Perspective of the Developing World – Asia

P. Ratanakul*

One of the privileges of being the last speaker is that after the presentations of the preceding distinguished speakers there is little more to say. However, I shall make some additional comments on the meeting in general and then say something about the main ethical issues in health policies confronted by the developing nations, particularly Thailand.

During the last three days we have discussed in depth and from different perspectives the main ethical issues that affect health policy in the developed nations. Even if there is not yet consensus on the resolution of these issues, we are now very well aware of their implications and complexity. Above all, we know what to avoid in the determination of health policy, though we may not yet be clear about what health policy should provide for in every respect.

This meeting had a regional purpose, with particular reference to North America and Europe. Yet its outcome is of great relevance to developing nations, because with modernization of medicine and technologies they will be faced with similar ethical issues.

I have noticed that in this CIOMS meeting, and in many meetings in the West concerned with bioethics, discussions on ethics and human values usually concentrate more on the values of justice and of human rights, that is to say, on what we must get from society. No one would dispute the importance of these two ethical and human values. But, for us in the East, there is another human value that should be fostered both in formulating health policy and in the practice of modern medicine. This value has been central to the teachings of the great religions, like Christianity and Buddhism. It is the ideal of compassion or loving kindness. It is a self-giving, self-denying, voluntary sacrifice of our own rights beyond what is socially obligated. Compassion is an act of generosity of spirit. It embraces justice, but at the same time goes beyond it. When a nurse stays with her patient, who needs her, night and day, forgoing rest and the company of her family, this is an act of compassion or self-denial, assuming a burden she is not socially obliged to bear. To pursue the ideal of compassionate service is to transcend concern for justice and individual rights; it is to be unconcerned whether one is getting what one deserves, being treated fairly, or securing what one rightfully claims. Indeed, medicine itself in the East and the West was originally inspired by this ideal of compassion. Medicine was developed to give loving service to suffering humanity. But today, I fear, this human value is in danger of being lost in the practice of modern

* Director, Research Center of Southeast Asian Cultures, Institute of Language and Culture for Rural Development, Mahidol University, Salaya, Thailand.

199

medicine. Therefore, it must be fostered as the best human value along with justice and human rights.

Now, let me turn briefly to some of the main ethical issues that the developing nations are facing. We must understand that medicine and technologies in these countries are not as developed and not at the same stage as in the developed nations. Therefore the ethical problems that stem from the use of high technologies, which we have discussed at the meeting, are much less common yet in many developing nations. In Thailand, for example, genetic testing and organ transplantation are still very rare. If, in the future, organ transplant services become common, there should be no serious difficulty as regards organ donation. Our culture and religious tradition stress the notion of merit and are less concerned about the sanctity and integrity of the self. To give one's life to save the life of the other is a meritorious act that will ensure a good reward in the future life. Accordingly, more Thais are now donating their bodies to medical schools for the advancement of medical science.

In the case of the elderly, a subject of much discussion at the meeting, we in Thailand are not likely to face the problem of Europe and North America. The life-span in our society is shorter and the ratio of the aged to the young in the total population has not yet reached the point at which problems begin. Furthermore, Thai culture, permeated by Buddhism, gives due regard to the aged and admonishes the young people, in particular, to show respect and gratitude to the elderly. This is the basis of the moral obligation of the young to care for the aged. To take good care of the aged, we believe, is a meritorious act that will reward us both in this life and after life. Thus in Thailand the young people look upon it as a privilege to have the elderly stay with them, even if it causes economic difficulties. While the country is moving forward towards modernity Thai public sentiment still continues to uphold this traditional value. Last year when we went to the Parliament to defend the University's budget, and the Medical School had asked for funds to buy a rather expensive life-support system for elderly patients, all the members of the budget scrutiny committee readily approved it, simply because the elderly patient commanded priority in their view. Of course, one cannot predict what the attitude of the future generation will be should we continue to face economic and unemployment problems while many more people live into old age. It will be interesting to observe how this traditional cultural value will be maintained in the face of new reality.

The most important issue relating to health and health policy in developing nations, as I see it, is the problem of the allocation of medical resources. It concerns the grave shortage of resources and inadequacies in needed services. In Thailand, for example, 80% of the population lives in villages. When I use the term "village" you should not think about the kind of village you would find in Switzerland, Holland or the United States. It is the village as it exists in India, Nigeria and Pakistan. Nearly all of the people in the villages are poor and uneducated, and their life-span is rather short. They need health care services more than city people do. However, 60% of all Thai government health personnel, and 70% of doctors and nurses, are concentrated in the metropolitan area, which has the most expensive transposed technologies and where the large public and private hospitals are built. This imbalance, I am afraid, is caused by the uncritical adoption of Western models of health-care systems, with concentration on high technology, research and hospital-oriented medicine. Following these models has led many developing nations to formulate health policies that neglect the principles of justice and compassion and do not ensure, therefore, that health resources are fairly distributed to the people of the different societal sectors.

Justice, the basic human value, is here understood as equal treatment, not only in the amount and nature of medical resources made available to the poor but also in the mode and manner of the service given. I have to emphasize equal treatment in mode and manner, because in developing nations usually the poor and people with low incomes have unpleasant experiences in hospital. They have to wait very long in crowded waiting-rooms but receive brief attention from doctors and also are subjected to impolite words and sometimes cold and harsh attitudes from medical personnel. All too often, the mode and the manner of treatment for the poor is degrading, humiliating, and dehumanizing. Thus in pursuing the ideal of justice, developing nations must ensure that these people are treated equally, with justice and compassion.

But even when there is concern for justice and compassion in the formulation of health policy, the other problem the developing nations are facing has to do with the implementation of policies, i.e. lack of serious commitment from governments and lack of competent manpower to implement the policies. In formulating health policy developing nations should not follow Western models concentrating on high-technology and hospital-oriented medicine. Most people in developing nations are ill and dying because of malnutrition, and lack of clean water resources, sanitation and knowledge. Obviously, most of their diseases could be prevented. Thus to serve the health needs of their people the developing nations must take account of this reality, the needs of communities, in the formulation of health policy.

In conclusion, the most important issue concerning health policy in the developing countries is imbalance in the allocation of medical resources and the unnecessary persistence of inadequacies in basic services. This problem is likely to remain a moral issue for a long time. Many developing countries tend to devote more funds and medical efforts to the diseases of the few, such as cancer and heart disease, while the majority are suffering and dying from lack of basic health care and maintenance. It is like serving a ten-course banquet just for a few in a society where many cannot afford even the bare necessities. It seems to me that to raise the general level of health in the developing nations the first need is for health education and preventive health-care, since environment and behaviour are the principal determinants of health and life expectancy. The availability of facilities for personal medical care plays a relatively small part. In allocating funds for health care, then,

201

more should be given to sanitation, immunization, better nutrition, and teaching better health habits; in particular, much more needs to be allocated to maternal and child care services. More should be expended on health maintenance programmes than on catastrophic medicine, and more to training paramedics to staff rural clinics and public health centres than to training doctors and nurses for hospital medicine.

Let me now turn to CIOMS. I must commend CIOMS for its plan to extend to the developing nations the International Dialogue on Ethics, Human Values and Health Policy, to stimulate and promote more interest and concern among policymakers in these countries for the needed relationship between values and health policy. As you are well aware, many developing countries have uncritically adopted Western medical models, and health policies are usually formulated without concern for ethics and human values. I am sure that the CIOMS meeting will make health policymakers from the developing countries more aware of the ethical issues arising from the use of high technology and the inseparability of health policy and human values.

This international dialogue must be extended to the developing nations because many of them have a long cultural history and tradition, which can be useful to the world community in its efforts to resolve new ethical issues in the practice of modern medicine. Their contributions may be made through international meetings as well as transcultural research.

Finally I commend CIOMS for its other plan — the organization of a special meeting in Thailand in 1988. The topic of the meeting — Ethics and Family Planning — is a very sensitive one in developing nations, where traditions and cultural values tend to be in conflict with this modern concern. The topic has not yet been freely and openly discussed for the public.

Perspective of an East-European Country — Poland

Magdalena Sokołowska*

Introduction

The international dialogue on health policy, ethics and human values established by CIOMS is a pioneering undertaking of great significance. CIOMS seems to be especially suitable to lead such action because it is a nongovernmental organization involving experts from all over the world and because of its multi- and inter-disciplinary character. I am pleased to participate in this conference. One finds here understanding, mutual respect, and quite a unique openness and willingness to learn new ideas from one another.

Nevertheless, it is not easy to speak on the last day of the conference. Much has been said already; there would be hardly time to discuss new questions. And first of all I have been given a difficult task: whereas the topics of the three other speakers are related to their professional domains (policymaking, health profession and ethics) I am supposed to present "an Eastern European country perspective".

Probably it should serve as some kind of general introduction and information before entering more specialized areas of "Eastern Europe". I understand that this is an initial stage of involvement of the specialists from "the East" in the activity of CIOMS. However, there could be countless "perspectives", depending upon the native country of the speaker and his/her background and interests. Therefore, it is hardly possible to expect any "representativeness" of my speech either for Eastern Europe or even for my native country, Poland. However, several facts and observations which I shall mention are probably relevant for various countries, both Eastern and Western.

I should add that I am neither an ethicist nor a policymaker, and nor am I a health professional. I am an empirically minded social researcher. Among other things, this means that I am particularly interested in the actual functioning of professed goals, objectives, legal norms, philosophies, ideologies, etc. I study their actual social consequences, their "social surrounding". It is obvious that ethics involves not only normative but also empirical issues. This fact has not always been remembered, however.

I should like to address myself to two questions: (1) the relevance of the slogan "your health in your hands" in Poland today, and (2) the universal question of the individualistic versus the group orientation of

---

* Professor, Institute of Philosophy and Sociology, Polish Academy of Sciences, Warsaw, Poland.

medical doctors in Western cultural circles. First, I am going to characterize briefly living conditions in Poland.

Some Characteristics of Poland

Poland is a middle-sized Central European country with a centrally planned economy. The health care system is highly centralized and bureaucratized. Generally, the systems that are centrally planned seem to be useful "in societies whose stage of development is such that the most widespread problems lie in health care tasks of the first order, tasks involving the application of comparatively straightforward techniques for the prevention and cure of clear-cut disease entities. Such systems are capable of spectacular advances — for example, the mass vaccination of populations, or the elimination of infectious or parasitic diseases — as has been observed in Cuba, in China, or in devastated Poland after World War II. However, such systems are less capable of dealing efficiently with unexpected problems, e.g. unexpected epidemics, or with new types of medical problem related to chronic illness and/or disability".[1]

The organization of the health system in Poland is not exceptional for the prevailing political and socio-economic system. All other formal structures, except the Roman Catholic Church, are organized "vertically". "Horizontal" links are non-existent or weak. "Community" — in the Western sense — hardly exists.

Sociological studies comparing ways of life of the Poles with those of Finns, Germans, French or Americans point out that the social, cultural and health needs of Poles today are almost identical with those of the others. However, there is a wide gap between the needs and the ability to meet them. Over the last 20 years, expenditure on health care as a proportion of Poland's national income has been running at around 3–4%.[2]

The most important components of the standards of living of the population: food supply, housing and environmental policy are deeply unsatisfactory.[3] A full-employment policy has certain negative effects on workers' health,[4] and the national economy is stagnating.

Mortality indicators are consistent with this picture. The infant mortality rate is excessively high for a European country: about 18–20 per 1 000 live births. The death rates of Polish men are rising. They turned upward in 1972, increasing to 11.9% by 1979. Middle-aged men are the most severely affected. In 1976 and 1977 male mortality in Poland was the highest in Europe — 10.3%. Expectation of life at 35 years for males was 27.6 in 1960 but only 26.3 in 1980 — a fall of 3.01%, the second worst in Europe.[5, 6]

Polish intellectuals enjoy high social standing. Their involvement in practical "problem-solving" at the societal level is one of their specific traits. Therefore, I also belong to those with "dirty hands", according to Dr de Wachter's expression.

"Your Health in Your Hands?"*

It seems that the emergence of slogans that represent health as our individual responsibility is closely related to the failure of social institutions responsible for realizing the proud slogan launched after World War II: "the right to health". The continuing crisis of the Welfare State results in a shift of its responsibilities to informal domains — family, self-help groups, etc. It is obvious that much depends on behavioural and cultural factors. At the same time, however, it is apparent that individual habits and lifestyles are strongly influenced by the formal institutions of a given society. The more powerful the institutions — especially if they are not in competition with one another — the less the chances of alternative choices and solutions. The Polish population has little or no control over the most important components of living standards: food supply, housing and environmental pollution. Moreover, even some behavioural factors destructive of health cannot be changed by individual effort. For example, a Polish consumer has very limited choice regarding nutrition; he lives under continuing stress, smokes cigarettes and drinks vodka, of which there is always a good supply and is among the easiest available products in the State-run shops. Until the government intervenes, there is little a citizen can do.

Sociological analysis suggests that viewing health as an individual responsibility quite likely over-estimates the magnitude of the health benefits that would result from personal habit changes. Second, this view of health tends to overlook or misconstrue the nature of societal constraints on individual will, and hence fails to specify the sociological conditions under which millions of individuals would be able to change their lives significantly, and the role *social* conditions have in maintaining unhealthy behaviour and attitudes. Finally, the focus on individual decision-making de-emphasises the role of collective efforts, of *public* policy, in securing higher health standards. Our thesis defines a more ethical and feasible national policy than the policy of health as individual responsibility.[7] Seat-belts do a thousand times more for safer driving than driver education does.

The notion of health as an individual responsibility underplays the role of society in creating conditions under which individuals both need to and are able to mobilize their will-power and to ignore the constraints societal factors impose on individual efforts. The only effective way to express our will is through collective action.

Individualistic and Group Orientation of Medical Doctors

The fundamental dividing line between doctors is determined by the style of their medical orientation.[8] There are two basic styles of medical

---

* In this part the author has assumed the role of devil's advocate in order to make the point sharp. Therefore, the obverse of the issue — success of individual efforts, the possibilities in Poland of citizens' actions, such actions themselves, etc. — are not discussed in the present text.

orientation — the individualistic orientation and the mass orientation, depending upon which constitutes the point of reference: the individual or the group. The individualistic orientation corresponds to the traditional character of medical knowledge; its conceptual apparatus is related to the individual, and the fundamental unit of analysis is a singular organism. Mass orientation shifts the point of interest towards the group, changing the fundamentals of the way of thinking and becoming a qualitatively different kind of medicine.

A "typical" doctor is a healer of sick individuals. Owing to this role, the doctor occupies, in all societies, the highest, or almost the highest, position according to the social scales of occupational prestige. He is the only professional defender of the sick, the disabled, the old. He must always, under all circumstances, place his patient's interests above all other values. Such doctors constitute a main body of the medical profession in any society. Nothing indicates that the societal need for the individual healer may decrease. Rather, a reverse phenomenon is observed. It results from the growth of the technical-medical possibilities, of achievements, and one observes an increasing trend towards assigning individual psychological problems to medical doctors.

Doctors who think in categories of the group constitute everywhere a minority among all doctors. It is not easy to be a doctor of public health, or social or community medicine. The medical school enforces the individualistic ideology and, consequently, strongly influences the students. The doctor is unprepared for a job calling for a group orientation. Above all, he must force himself to overcome the doctor's nature.

Concern over the proper use of social resources becomes a problem of the protection of society rather than of the individual, and requires a separate ethics. The problem of rationing health-care services becomes crucial. Making such decisions is extraordinarily difficult and it raises serious questions about the adequacy of official medical ethics. Two days ago, Dr Capron observed that several crucial issues in medicine suffer from a lack of philosophical base. I would add that it is perhaps official medical ethics that suffers mostly from it. The CIOMS Programme on an International Dialogue on Health Policy, Ethics and Human Values is the most suitable mechanism for an attempt to reformulate medical ethics to take account of the need to protect society as well as the individual.

References

[1] Friedson, E. Application of organizational theory: models of organization of service for health care. In: *Health, Medicine, Sociology*, Sokołowska, M., Ostrowksa A. & Hołówka, J. (eds). Reidel and Polish Scientific Publishers, Dordrecht 1976.
[2] Sokołowska, M. & Moskalewicz, B. Health Sector Structures: The Case of Poland. *Social Science and Medicine 24* (9):763–75 (1987).

3   Health and Health Protection of the Polish Population. Report from Poland. *International Journal of Health Services, 13* (3):487–513 (1983).

4   Gniazdowski, A. *Full-employment policy in Poland and some of its effects related to workers' health.* Paper presented at a WHO meeting on Unemployment, Poverty and Quality of Working Life. Copenhagen, WHO Regional Office for Europe, 1987 (ICP/HSR 818/24).

5   Brzezinski, Z. *Mortality in the European Region.* Copenhagen, WHO Regional Office for Europe, 1985 (ICP/EXM 001 g07). Unpublished document.

6   *The health burden of social inequities.* Report based on the proceedings of a WHO meeting. Copenhagen, WHO Regional Office for Europe, 1986 (ICP/HSR 804 m01), p.p. 157–70.

7   Etzioni, A. Individual Will and Social Conditions: Toward An Effective Health Maintenance Policy. *The Annals of the American Academy of Political and Social Science,* Philadelphia, 1978.

8   Sokołowska, M., Two Basic Types of Medical Orientation. *Social Science and Medicine,* 7:807–15 (1973).

Perspective of an East-European Country—The German Democratic Republic

S. M. Rapoport*

I should like to give you a very short account which Dr. Luther and I have prepared on the positions and experiences of the German Democratic Republic (GDR), entitled: Improvement of life style and life quality — an essential task of health policy of the GDR.

Lifestyles and health hazards have been increasingly the subject of discussions of health planners, physicians, demographers and philosophers in the GDR. In 1983 we had a national conference on socialist lifestyle and health; in 1985 a symposium dealt with "youth and healthy lifestyle". For 1988 a further symposium on this subject is planned. It may also be mentioned that the 31st session of the WHO Regional Committee for Europe, which discussed especially health education and lifestyle, was held in the GDR. Important aspects of the charter for health promotion of the conference of Ottawa have been publicized in our country.

What I will have to say has been prepared beforehand and there may be some overlap with opinions voiced by others: I am very grateful to the preceding speaker, Professor Sokolowska, who has stated important general viewpoints. From our presentation it will be evident that each socialist country exhibits specific features with respect to approaches, legislation and other aspects.

In the view prevailing in the GDR, lifestyles are determined both by the conditions of life and by the qualities and attitudes of individuals. Any improvement of the health situation must therefore encompass both the individual and society. Any ethical appeal must be directed to both of them. The mastery of the relationship between the individual and society is of course the most difficult task for any policy to improve lifestyles. At present, we take the view that a realistic policy should be aimed at the optimal utilization of the potential life-time. This task includes elimination of causes of premature and avoidable death, prevention and mitigation of chronic disease and ailments, and the creation of conditions that enable every individual to make the best use of his faculties even if they are reduced in quality or quantity.

To establish such conditions, society has a duty to guarantee social security for everybody, including adequate housing, food, comprehensive health care, education, and full employment. These issues are the core of government policy. Of course, a universal precondition, which unites us all, is the joint effort of all societies for a peaceful future of the

* Professor, Institut für Biochemie des Bereichs Medizin (Charité) der Humboldt-Universität zu Berlin, Berlin, German Democratic Republic.

world and, in particularly, the prevention of a nuclear catastrophe. Even the existence of the perpetual threat of nuclear warfare has been shown to be a detrimental factor on the outlook of life, even of children, in many empirical studies, apart from the fact that armaments by necessity reduce the resources for life improvement.

Among the important responsibilities of society we consider the development of medical science and utilization of its international achievements for the benefits of each individual — and this costs a lot of money, the information and education of the people to manage their conduct of life in an optimal manner, and the establishment of conditions that minimize harmful influences on the micro- and the macro-environment. An important consideration in the GDR is the concerted effort of society to create a general atmosphere of respect for, and solidarity with, each individual, in particular, the handicapped and the elderly. A whole system has been created to maintain their contacts with the former working-place, the neighbourhood, and with one another, to avoid isolation. Prolongation of life beyond the natural life-span, as indicated by statistics, is not in the foreground of present-day medical research or health care in the GDR.

Of course, it has to be realized that collective health is composed of the health of each individual. Therefore, lifestyle and the attitude of the individual play a key role in the progress of health. Appreciation and realization of the lifestyle which maintains or even improves health is based on knowledge, responsibility, and a high valuation of the purpose of life. Such a lifestyle expresses, of course, a free individual decision, which by prolonging the period of active life enlarges the sphere of action and influence of a person, provided society offers him this possibility.

Both from a religious and a non-religious point of view, each human life is a unique opportunity, leading to the ethical conclusion that we should make the most of it. This includes, for most people, a lifestyle conducive to health. Besides a duty to oneself, there is the family and society, which suffer in various respects from an inconsiderate way of dealing with one's health.

The emphasis on individual responsibility for maintenance of health in no way reduces the responsibility of society to provide social security. One might raise the question whether diseases caused by the person's own fault — overeating, alcoholism, drugs, negligence, or ignorance — constitute an abuse of the health system and whether the coverage should include all types of health-related expense such as that for dentures, eye-glasses, hearing aids and other prostheses, and whether all medicines should be free of charge. We, in the GDR, take a very firm position on these questions, i.e., to provide comprehensive care without exception. Within this framework a continuous effort is made to educate physicians, patients, and the entire population to increase their responsibility for healthful life and the prevention and early diagnosis of disease.

However, a realistic assessment of the health situation and lifestyle gives a very sobering picture. The individual energy intake in the GDR is well above that recommended by nutritionists and I will just state one single figure — that of fat is about 160% of that recommended; 20% of men and more than 30% of women are overweight. The consumption of alcohol has been increasing steadily and exceeds by now 10 litres a year per person. Cigarette smoking, particularly among the young, has not been significantly reduced. The incidence of diabetes is nearly 4% and the rate of mortality from heart disease has been declining only lately. Obviously the methods used so far to educate and train the population and, in particular the young generation, have not been successful and I want to add that I think this is a problem that concerns us all. Of course there are the skills of the advertising experts but this is not science as yet, and not all advertising is as successful as it is made out to be — I think this is an area of research that needs international exchange.

At present, a new concerted effort is being made through all media to make headway. Promotion of a healthy lifestyle is not restricted to health personnel. Teachers, psychologists, sociologists, well-known sportsmen, singers and other people who may attract the young generation participate in this effort and we shall see what effect this will have. The attempt is made to replace the emphasis on the menaces of health hazards by a positive approach which stresses the joys of health; instead of pedantic prescriptions for a reformed life, stress is put on a variety of possibilities of healthy lifestyles.

With the rising level of societal development, the value of individual life increases and, of course, its cost, and medicine is challenged to do its utmost to save and prolong each life. The accomplishment of this postulate is nowhere a complete reality, but everywhere a compelling task, which requires ever-increasing efforts and resources, owing to the progress of medical science and technology and rising demands. Therefore, in the GDR, there is envisaged a continuous rise of expenditure on health without any thought of reducing or restricting it. We realize that extending life also brings with it the possibility of an increased proportion of handicapped individuals. This problem is partly met by the creation of a general atmosphere of solicitude as well as a comprehensive system of care for the various groups of handicapped. The idea of an unworthy life is for us particularly abhorrent in view of the mass murder, the so-called euthanasia of the handicapped, practised wholesale in Nazi Germany and in which medical people and institutions were involved.

Human life may be considered under biological, social and ethical aspects, and I should like to close by citing a quotation of the great Tolstoy, who wrote once: "Man can consider himself as an animal among animals, as a member of his family, of society, of the people he belongs to, but he can and must also consider himself as part of the whole world. Therefore, reasonable man must perform what the mathematicians call 'integration'. That is, he must establish a relationship not only with the phenomena of life nearest to him but also with the entire world in its temporal and spatial infinity" (L. N. Tolstoy, Polnoje sobranije sotschineni, Vol. 35, p. 161). The limitation of the life-span, which is a powerful force for utilizing the personal life-time in an optimal manner, is transcended by the feeling of continuity of humanity. Mastery of one's own life — and that of society in harmony with nature — is, I think, the guideline for an optimal lifestyle.

CLOSING OF CONFERENCE

J. van Londen
Director-General of Health, Ministry of Welfare, Health and Cultural Affairs, Rijswijk, Netherlands

I am very impressed by the summary of Professor Bryant. Speaking on behalf of our State Secretary, Mr Dees, who was your host, I want to say a few words.

I think that you as participants in this conference have a right to ask the question of your host country: What are your interests, having this conference in your country? What do you think are the benefits for your country to have this CIOMS conference in the Netherlands? The first answer is that the Netherlands firmly believes in international cooperation and also firmly believes that the only way to peace, and equity, and solidarity is through international cooperation. But there is a second reason. Nowadays we have a discussion going on about the relation of cost containment to health policy — cost containment in the health sector and our health policy. This week, Members of Parliament have requested the Government to put forward a policy document on the relation between cost containment in health care and basic health policy. In the health-policy paper, it has to be shown what are the principles of our health policy, what are the ethical issues, what is our value system in the Netherlands. It is very important that in this week's debate in Parliament our Prime Minister, as leader of the Government, was requested to ensure that cost containment in the health care sector should be dealt with only in the perspective of a health policy. I trust that our Government will publish such a paper today and that Parliament will discuss the health policy paper and the proposals of cost containment for the coming years in relation to each other.

We are indeed faced with many ethical issues in the Netherlands, as every other country is, and the four areas you have dealt with in this conference — screening, transplantation, the elderly and lifestyles — are very actual, burning issues.

How do they fit in, and how does the Government of the Netherlands want to work in this international system? Of course, we start with WHO and we respect, as other countries do, the international value system of WHO. I think that also CIOMS can contribute to elaborating on this value system of WHO. Equity, social equity, is an important issue in this respect. I should like to mention that a few months ago the Government organized a national conference on "Inequities in health and in health care in the Netherlands", and you may think — Dr Bryant mentioned that the Netherlands is so well organized — that there is no inequity in the Netherlands, but this is not true!

We are well organized, but there is also some inequity — we have to confess — and we want to work with it and on it. And we have to have the support of international cooperation, of WHO and CIOMS.

I was prepared to say something on the continuity of the discussions of CIOMS, but I see that Dr Bryant has formulated it as a goal, as a recommendation, so I can only conclude that the Netherlands Government wants to stress this recommendation and, being now in a position this year to act as President of the World Health Assembly, I can assure you that I will bring these ideas to the Director-General of WHO, Dr Mahler, and from the Netherlands Government to Dr Asvall, Director of the WHO Regional Office for Europe, and from my own position to my own Government.

I want to thank you all for coming to the Netherlands.

I picked up one idea this morning, and that was the role of philosophy and philosophers. I want to stress that in our opinion, in the opinion of the Ministry of Welfare, Health and Cultural Affairs, more research on ethical issues is needed in the Netherlands, more systematic research is needed. We have in the Netherlands a national, but not governmental, institute for research on ethics, which is situated in Maastricht. Also some of the universities play an important role in research in ethics and we want to have this research done in a systematic way, and we want to have our Health Council and the newly established Research Council do some guiding work for making the work which is already being done in the Netherlands more systematic. And perhaps we should have — if it is at all possible — new civil servants in my Ministry, and if we can have new civil servants one of them must be a philosopher.

Thank you very much. I wish you a happy and safe return to your countries.

F. Vilardell
President, Council of International Organizations for Medical Sciences

Dr van Londen, Members of CIOMS, Ladies and Gentlemen.

Dr van Londen's words are bringing to an end this CIOMS Conference on Health Policy, Ethics and Human Values — European and North American Perspectives, which for four days of strenuous work has brought together physicians, lawyers, philosophers, sociologists and policymakers interested in our common goal of health for all.

May I express the gratitude of CIOMS and, I am sure, of all of us to the Dutch Ministry of Welfare, Health and Culture, in the person of Dr van Londen, Director General, and to the local organizing committee, so ably chaired by Mrs Johanna Helena Krijnen and Professor Maurice de Wachter. Most especially we must thank Professor Albert van der Werff, who conceived the idea of inviting CIOMS to Noordwijk.

In this chapter of thanks, you will agree that a special place has been earned by Mrs Anne-Mieke Alkemade and her efficient staff, as well as Miss van der Wejden, Banquet Manager of this hotel, who has provided with her staff the basic facilities for many pleasant opportunities for getting together. Special thanks should be given to Dr John Bryant, Chairman of the Programme Committee, and the soul of this meeting, for preparing a programme of such quality and interest. From my own personal viewpoint, I cannot imagine a better way to start my term as President of CIOMS and hope that this is also the feeling of the CIOMS Vice-Presidents, Drs Motzel, Corvera and Thangaraj.

Last but not least, our thanks to Dr Zbigniew Bankowski, Executive Secretary of CIOMS, for his painstaking efforts to make this meeting successful. In this he has been ably aided by Mrs Kathryn Chalaby-Amsler, CIOMS Secretary.

Participants from 35 countries have registered at this conference, which is a follow-up, from the viewpoint of the Western World, of the Athens Conference on Health Policy, Ethics and Human Values — An International Dialogue. As is customary for CIOMS, since its foundation by WHO and Unesco, we have tried to provide a wide international forum for the exploration of scientific, social, legal, and, above all, humanistic implications of these problems. This multidisciplinary approach provides insights into issues that cannot in any way be the exclusive concern of one single profession. Even in this atmosphere of frank and vivid discussions, it would be premature to draw definitive conclusions from these dialogues, which will be pursued in successive conferences with the aim of providing as wide as possible perspectives to those who have to establish policies as harmoniously as it may be permitted. In the meantime, a CIOMS meeting is already announced for June 19–24, 1988 in Bangkok under the general title: Ethics and Human Values in Family Planning.

To all contributors, to all speakers, rapporteurs and participants, and to the audience, my heartiest thanks. I would also like to assure our

215

Dutch hosts that I presume the very informed consent of all of us in announcing that our hearts have now been very successfully and firmly transplanted into Holland!

LIST OF PARTICIPANTS

AARTSEN, J.G.M. Department of Health Care Professions and Training, Ministry of Welfare, Health and Cultural Affairs, Rijswijk, Netherlands

ABDUSSALAM, M. Advisory Committee on Health Research, World Health Organization, Geneva, Switzerland

ABULFADL, M.A.M. Faculty of Medicine, Cairo University, Cairo, Egypt

ADADEVOH, B.K. Ebute-Metta, Lagos State, Nigeria

AKVELD, J. Erasmus University, Rotterdam, Netherlands

ALHO, A. Regional Committee for Ethics in Medical Research, Orthopaedic Service, Ullevaal Hospital, Oslo, Norway

AL SAYEGH, M.O. Ministry of Health, Department of Forensic Medicine, Riyadh, Saudi Arabia

ANDERSEN, D. Department of Surgical Gastroenterology, Odense Hospital, Odense, Denmark

BAKKER, P.G. International Union Against Venereal Diseases and the Treponematoses, The Hague, Netherlands

BANKOWSKI, Z. Council for International Organizations of Medical Sciences (CIOMS), Geneva, Switzerland

BARZELATTO, J. Special Programme of Research, Development and Research Training in Human Reproduction, World Health Organization, Geneva, Switzerland

de BEAUFORT, I. Institute of Bioethics, Maastricht, Netherlands

BÉGIN, M. Women's Studies, University of Ottawa, Ottawa, Ontario, Canada

BELCHIOR, M. Council for International Organizations of Medical Sciences (CIOMS), Rio de Janeiro, Brazil

BETTEX, M.C. World Federation of Associations of Paediatric Surgeons, Berne, Switzerland

BLACK, SIR DOUGLAS. Whitchurch-on-Thames, Reading, England

BLAND, J.H. Programme Support Service, World Health Organization, Geneva, Switzerland

BÖKKERINK, J.M. Rehabilitation Council, Tilburg, Netherlands

BONÉ, E. Université de Louvain, Centre d'Etudes Bioéthiques, Brussels, Belgium

BORST-EILERS, E. Health Council of the Netherlands, The Hague, Netherlands

BOS, M.A. Ministry of Welfare, Health and Cultural Affairs, Rijswijk, Netherlands

BOTTA, A. Federation of Hungarian Medical Societies, Budapest, Hungary

BRENNINKMEIJER-RUTTEN, M.B.E.G. Steering Committee on the Policy for Disabled, Ministry of Welfare, Health and Cultural Affairs, Rijswijk, Netherlands

BRYANT, J.H. Department of Community Health Sciences, Aga Khan University, Karachi, Pakistan

BULTMAN, J. Dutch Sick Fund Council, Amstelveen, Netherlands

CALLAHAN, D. The Hastings Center, Briarcliff Manor, New York, U.S.A.

CALLAHAN, S. Department of Psychology, Mercy College, Dobbs Fully, New York, U.S.A.

CAPRON, A.M. Law Center, University of Southern California, Los Angeles, California, U.S.A.

CHERMAK, G. Kellogg Foundation, Washington State University, Pullman, Washington, U.S.A.

CLETON, F.J. International Union Against Cancer, Department of Clinical Oncology, University Hospital, Leiden, Netherlands

CORVERA BERNARDELLI, J. Academia Nacional de Medicina, Mexico City, Mexico

COURVOISIER, B. Swiss Academy of Medical Sciences, Geneva, Switzerland

DANIELSSON, H. Swedish Medical Research Council, Stockholm, Sweden

DESCAMPS-LATSCHA, B. Reseach INSERM, Hôpital Necker, Paris, France

van der DOES DE WILLEBOIS, A.J. Medical Association of Holland, Holy See, Utrecht, Netherlands

DOXIADIS, S. Foundation for Research in Childhood, Athens, Greece

van DUIJN, P. Medical Section, Dutch Academy of Sciences, Oegstgeest, Netherlands

DUNNE, J.F. Pharmaceuticals, World Health Organization, Geneva, Switzerland

DUPUIS, H. Faculty of Medicine, University of Leiden, Netherlands

van EEK, W. Occupational Health Care Service, The Hague, Netherlands

ESKEDAL, T. Etisk Komite Norway, Stavanger, Norway

ESKOLA, J. National Board of Health, Helsinki, Finland

van ETTEN, G.M. Staff Bureau for Health Policy Development, Ministry of Welfare, Health and Cultural Affairs, Rijswijk, Netherlands

FADEN, R. Johns Hopkins University, School of Hygiene and Public Health, Baltimore, Maryland, U.S.A.

FARBER, J. World Medical Association, Chambre syndicale des Médecins de l'Agglomération bruxelloise, Brussels, Belgium

FARSANG, C. Federation of Hungarian Medical Societies, Budapest, Hungary

FESTEN, C.A.W.M. Royal Netherlands Academy of Arts and Sciences, Amsterdam, Netherlands

FISEK, N.H. Turkish Medical Association, Ankara, Turkey

FISHER, E. Department of Psychology, Washington University, St. Louis, Missouri, U.S.A.

GELLHORN, A. Medical Affairs, State of New York Department of Health, Albany, New York, U.S.A.

GEVERS, J.K.M. Dutch Health Law Association, Institute of Social Medicine, Amsterdam, Netherlands

GOROVITZ, S. College of Arts and Sciences, Syracuse University, Syracuse, New York, U.S.A.

HACHEN, H.J. International Rehabilitation Medicine Association, Spinal Injuries Center, Geneva, Switzerland

HALLIDAY, N.R. Department of Health and Social Security, London, England

HATHOUT, H. Faculty of Medicine, University of Kuwait, Kuwait

HASLINGHUIS, E.J.D. General Health Care, Ministry of Welfare, Health and Cultural Affairs, Rijswijk, Netherlands

ten HAVE, H. Department of Health Care Ethics, University of Limburg, Maastricht, Netherlands

HEIM, E. Swiss National Research Council, Psychiatrische Universitäts-poliklinik, Berne, Switzerland

HERMERÉN, G. Philosophy Department, Lund University, Lund, Sweden

HONINGS, B. Pontifical Commission for the Apostolate of Health Care Workers, Rome, Italy

HORST, J. Institute for Human Genetics, University of Münster, Münster, Federal Republic of Germany

JANSSENS, P.G. Royal Academics of Medicine of Belgium, 'S Gravenwezel, Belgium

JOKINEN, R. Finnish Medical Association, Helsinki, Finland

JONSEN, A. School of Medicine (and Ethics), University of California, San Francisco, California, U.S.A.

JURGENS, K. Advisory Council on Health Research, The Hague, Netherlands

KEOGH, A. Transplant Co-ordinator South-East/West Regions, London, England

KIMURA, R. Kennedy Institute of Ethics, Georgetown University, Washington, D.C., U.S.A.

KIT NIEUWENKAMP, J.W.H. Department of Health Care Professions and Training, Ministry of Welfare, Health and Cultural Affairs, Rijswijk, Netherlands

van der KLOOT MEIJBURG, H.H. Religious Ethical Affairs, Dutch Hospital Association, Utrecht, Netherlands

KOFLER, W. Department of Social Medicine, Ministry of Health, Innsbruck, Austria

KOIZUMI, A. Science Council of Japan, Tokyo, Japan

KOKKONEN, P. Department of Administration, National Board of Health, Helsinki, Finland

KORVER, A. League of Red Cross and Red Crescent Societies, Netherlands Red Cross, The Hague, Netherlands

KOSTER-DREESE, Y. Landelijk Patiënten/Consumenten Platform, Baarn, Netherlands

KRAMERS, W. Faculty of Medicine, University of Utrecht, Department of General Health Care and Epidemiology, Utrecht, Netherlands

KRIJNEN, J.H. Staff Bureau for Health Policy Development, Ministry of Welfare, Health and Cultural Affairs, Rijswijk, Netherlands

KROMWIJK, B. Eurotransplant Foundation, University Hospital Leiden, Leiden, Netherlands

KUUSKOSKI-VIKATMAA, E. Member of Parliament, Helsinki, Finland

LACQUET, A. Royal Academies of Medicine, Leuven, Belgium

LAST, J.M. School of Medicine, University of Ottawa, Ottawa, Ontario, Canada

LEENEN, H.J.J. Institute of Social Medicine, Amsterdam, Netherlands

van LEEUWEN, E. Faculty of Medicine, Free University, Amsterdam. Netherlands

LILJESTROM, M. Ministry of Social Affairs and Health, Helsinki, Finland

LINDQVIST, M. National Board of Health, Helsinki, Finland

LING, S.L. Ministry of Health, Singapore, Republic of Singapore

van LONDEN, J. Ministry of Welfare, Health and Cultural Affairs, Rijswijk, Netherlands

LUTHER, E. Universität Halle, Halle, German Democratic Republic

van MAANEN, H. National Nurses Association "Het Beterschap", Utrecht, Netherlands

MAGYAR, K. Federation of Hungarian Medical Societies, Budapest, Hungary

MANDEMA, E. Advisory Council on Health Research, The Hague, Netherlands

MARQUET, J. International Federation of Otorhinolaryngological Societies, Berchem-Antwerp, Belgium

MARTIN, J.F. Service de la Santé publique, Lausanne, Switzerland

MATTHEIS, R. Senate of Health and Social Affairs, Berlin (West)

McFARLANE, A.H. Health Sciences Centre, McMaster University, Hamilton, Ontario, Canada

MEINARDI, H. International League Against Epilepsy, Heemstede, Netherlands

de MELO, NEL CIVONE SOARES. Federal Council of Medicine, Rio de Janeiro, Brazil

MILLIEZ, J. Department of Obstetric Gynaecology, Centre Hospitalier Intercommunal, Créteil, France

MOTZEL, C. Medical Women's International Association, Cologne, Federal Republic of Germany

MULDER, J.M. Staff Bureau for Health Policy Development, Ministry of Welfare, Health and Cultural Affairs, Rijswijk, Netherlands

MÜLLER-FAHRENHOLZ, G. Evangelical Academy, Bad Segeberg, Federal Republic of Germany

MURDOCK, J. Health & Welfare Ministries, United Methodist Church, New York, New York, U.S.A.

MUSSCHENGA, A.W. Free University, Amsterdam, Netherlands

MUSIL, E. International Federation for Hygiene, Preventive Medicine and Social Medicine, Vienna, Austria

NICHOLSON, R.H. Institute of Medical Ethics, IME Publications Ltd., London, England

NIEDERLAND, T.R. Czechoslovak Medical Society, J.E. Purkyne/Federation of Medical Societies of Czechoslovakia, Bratislava, Czechoslovakia

NIERMEIJER, M.F. Clinical Genetics, Erasmus University, Rotterdam, Netherlands

NOACH, E.L. Netherlands Institute for Bioethics, Leiderdorp, Netherlands

NYS, H. Medical Law, Catholic University of Leuven, Leuven, Belgium

OSUNTOKUN, B.O. Neurology Unit, Department of Medicine, University of Ibadan, College of Medicine, Ibadan, Nigeria

OTTOSSON, J.O. Swedish Society of Medicine, Medical Ethics, Gothenburg, Sweden

PÉLICIER, Y. Service Psychiatrie, Faculté de Médecine, Hôpital Necker, Paris, France

PETERS, P.J.W. Department of Teratology, National Institute of Public Health and Environmental Hygiene, Bilthoven, Netherlands

PIJNEBURG, M. Department of Medical Ethics, University of Nijmegen, Nijmegen, Netherlands

PILOT, T. International Dental Federation, Gieten, Netherlands

PINET, G. Health Legislation, World Health Organization Regional Office for Europe, Copenhagen, Denmark

PROVÉ, G. Medical Mission Sisters, Amsterdam, Netherlands

PUTMAN-CRAMER, M. Nursing Home CICIAMS, Wassenaar, Netherlands

RAPOPORT, S.M. Coordinating Council for the Medical Societies of the German Democratic Republic, Berlin, German Democratic Republic

RATANAKUL, P. Bioethics Programme, Mahidol University, Salaya, Nakonpatom, Thailand de RIDDER, C. National Nurses Association "Het Beterschap", Utrecht, Netherlands

RIGTER, H. Health Council of the Netherlands, The Hague, Netherlands

RIIS, P. Danish Scientific-Ethical Committee, Herlev University Hospital, Herlev, Denmark

ROSCAM ABBING, E.W. Ministry of Welfare, Health and Cultural Affairs, Rijswijk, Netherlands

RUDOWSKI, W. Medical Section, Polish Academy of Sciences, Warsaw, Poland

SABATINI, J. Faculté de Médecine, Université de Lyon, Lyon, France

SCHARRER, S. Evangelical Academy Nordelbien, Bad Segeberg, Federal Republic of Germany

SCHROTEN, E. Centre for Bioethics and Medical Law, University of Utrecht, Utrecht, Netherlands

SIIM, J. CHR. The Royal Danish Academy of Sciences and Letters, Copenhagen, Denmark

SOKOŁOWSKA, M. Polish Academy of Sciences, Institute of Philosophy and Sociology, Warsaw, Poland

STEVENS, J.A.J. Dutch Catholic and Christian Medical Association, Arnhem, Netherlands

STRASSER, T. International Green Cross and World Hypertension League, Geneva, Switzerland

STUYT, L.B.J. The Netherlands Institute for Bioethics, The Hague, Netherlands

SUBEIHI, S. Ministry of Health, Amman, Jordan

THANGARAJ, R.H. International Leprosy Association, New Delhi, India

TRANÖY, K.E. Department of General Practice and Philosophy, University of Oslo, Oslo, Norway

TUORI, M.R. The Finnish Council for Health Education, Helsinki, Finland

VELDKAMP, H.R.G. Health Care, Professions and Training, Ministry of Welfare, Health and Cultural Affairs, Rijswijk, Netherlands

VERELST, R. Hospital Committee of the E.E.C., Heverlee, Belgium

VILARDELL, F. Council for International Organizations of Medical Sciences (CIOMS)/World Organization of Gastroenterology, Barcelona, Spain

VOUTILAINEN, P. The Lutherian Congregation of the City of Helsinki, Helsinki, Finland

de WACHTER, M.A.M. Institute for Bioethics, Maastricht, Netherlands

van der WAL, C.W. Division for Health Research TNO, Rijswijk, Netherlands

van der WERFF, A. Ministry of Welfare, Health and Cultural Affairs, Woubrugge, Netherlands

de WERT, G.M.W.R. Institute for Bioethics, Maastricht, Netherlands

WESTERBORN, O. Medical Ethics Committee, Swedish Medical Association, Örebro, Sweden

WIJNBERG, B. Staff Bureau for Policy Development, Ministry of Welfare, Health and Cultural Affairs, Rijswijk, Netherlands

de WIT-MULDER, M. Emancipation Council, The Hague, Netherlands

WITTEVEEN, P. Association for and of the Blind and Partially Sighted in the Netherlands (VNWB), Utrecht, Netherlands

ZAIMOV, K. Union of the Scientific Medical Societies, Sofia, Bulgaria